Tl

Supl
Gl

tu
Premiership &
Football League
Clubs
1996

EDITOR
John Robinson

Twelfth Edition

British Library Cataloguing in Publication Data

A catalogue record for this book is available from the British Library

ISBN 0-947808-46-9

Printed by Redwood Books, Kennet House, Kennet Way, Trowbridge, Wilts.

CONTENTS

FOREWORD

We are indebted to the staffs of the clubs featured in this guide for their cooperation and also to Michael Robinson (page layouts), Ceri Sampson (cover artwork), Kevin Norminton, Chris Ambler and Ken Ferris (photos).

When using the guide, please note that 'child' concessions generally include senior citizens also. A number of clubs had not set their 1995/96 Season admission prices when we completed the guide and where this is the case we have shown 1994/95 price information.

Disabled Supporters should note that we have, in conjunction with Shoot magazine, produced an entirely separate booklet, listing relevant information for all of the major League and Non-League clubs in Britain. This bi-annual was published in 1994, is priced at just 99p per copy and can be obtained from us post free.

Regular purchasers of this guide will notice that we have used a completely new set of ground photos to illustrate the incredible developments which have taken place over the last 2 or 3 years. However, ground moves and rebuilding are continuing apace and travelling fans may find that away sections and prices change during the course of the 1995/96 season.

Finally, we would like to wish our readers a happy and safe spectating season.

John Robinson
EDITOR

THE

NATIONAL FOOTBALL

STADIA

OF

BRITAIN

WELSH NATIONAL STADIUM

Re-Opened for Football: 31st May 1989	**Pitch Size**: 110 × 69yds
Location: Cardiff City Centre, CARDIFF	**Ground Capacity**: 51,374
Telephone: (01222) 390111 (Ground)	**Seating Capacity**: 42,355
Telephone: (01222) 372325 (F.A. of Wales)	(40,240 for Football Matches)
Address: The National Ground, Cardiff Arms Park, Westgate Street, CARDIFF, Wales	

GENERAL INFORMATION
Car Parking: City Centre Car Parks
Coach Parking: By Police Direction
Nearest Railway Station: 5-10 minutes walk
Nearest Bus Station: 5 minutes walk
Nearest Police Station: Cardiff Centre
Police Force: South Wales
Police Telephone No.: (01222) 222111

GROUND INFORMATION
Family Facilities: **Location of Stand**:
Lower Tier of North & South Stands
Capacity of Stand: Not Specified

DISABLED SUPPORTERS INFORMATION
Wheelchairs: Accommodated in Disabled Section - North Side of West Stand - space for 24 wheelchairs
Disabled Toilets: Yes

ADMISSION INFO (1995/96 PRICES)
Adult Seating: £6.00 - £20.00
Child Seating: Half-price in Family Enclosures
Programme Price: £2.00
FAX Number: (01222) 343961
Note: Prices vary depending on the opponents & type of game.

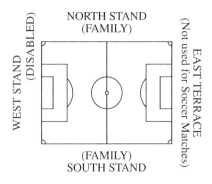

Travelling Supporters Information:
Routes: Exit M4 at Junction 29 and take A48(M) following signs for Cardiff City Centre (via A470). Use City Centre Public Car Parks.
From Cardiff Central Railway Station proceed past Bus Station, cross Wood Street and turn down Westgate Street (alongside the back of the Royal Hotel).

WEMBLEY STADIUM

Opened: 1923	**Ground Capacity**: 80,000
Location: Wembley, Middlesex HA9 0DW	**Seating Capacity**: 80,000
Telephone: Box Office (0181) 900-1234	**Record Attendance**: 100,000
Telephone: Administration (0181) 902-8833	**Pitch Size**: 115 × 75yds

GENERAL INFORMATION
Guided Tours Available: Telephone
(0181) 902-8833 (ext. 3346)
Parking: Car Park for over 7,000 vehicles
Nearest Railway Stations: Wembley Park,
Wembley Central, Wembley Complex (5-
10 minutes walk)
Nearest Police Station: Mobile Unit in
front of Twin Towers
**Police Force Responsible for Crowd
Control**: Metropolitan
Police Telephone No.: (0181) 900-7212

GROUND INFORMATION
All Sections of the Ground are Covered
Family Facilities: **Location of Stand**:
Family Enclosure, North Stand

DISABLED SUPPORTERS INFORMATION
Wheelchairs: Limited Facilities Available
Disabled Toilets: Yes
The Blind: No Special Facilities

ADMISSION INFO (1995/96 PRICES)
Admission £12.00 - £30.00; depending on the game and
ground position. Also a £1 per seat booking fee
(Accompanied Children - half price in family enclosure)

OLYMPIC WAY & TWIN TOWERS
(ROYAL BOX SIDE)   FAMILIES
NORTH STAND

(STADIUM OFFICE END)
WEST TERRACE

(PLAYERS TUNNEL END)
EAST TERRACE

SOUTH STAND

How to get to Wembley By Road

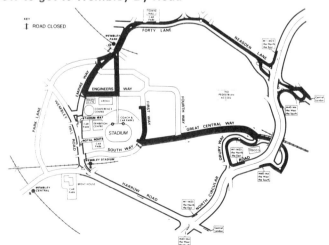

7

HAMPDEN STADIUM

Opened: 1903
Location: In the 'Mount Florida' area of Glasgow, South East of the River Clyde
Telephone: Administration (0141) 632-1275
Address: Hampden Park, Mount Florida, Glasgow   G42   9BA

Ground Capacity: 38,000
Seating Capacity: 38,000
Record Attendance: 150,239 (Scotland vs. England 17/4/37)
Pitch Size: 115 × 75yds
When development complete - capacity 60,000

GENERAL INFORMATION
Car Parking: Car Park for 1,200 vehicles
Coach Parking: Stadium Car Park
Nearest Railway Station: Mount Florida & Kings Park (both 5 minutes walk)
Nearest Police Station: Aikenhead Road, Glasgow G42
Police Force Responsible for Crowd Control: Strathclyde
Police Telephone No.: (0141) 422-1113

GROUND INFORMATION
Family Facilities: Location of Stand:
Varies from game to game
Capacity of Stand: -

DISABLED SUPPORTERS INFORMATION
Wheelchairs: Accommodated in Disabled Spectators Terrace: 54 Wheelchairs, 48 Ambulance Seated, 120 Ambulance Standing
Disabled Toilets: Yes, by Disabled Area
The Blind: Personal Commentaries

FAX Number: (0141) 636-1612

NORTH STAND

WEST STAND   EAST STAND

(DISABLED TERRACE)
SOUTH STAND
MOUNT FLORIDA   KINGS PARK

Travelling Supporters Information:
Routes: From the South: Take the A724 to the Cambuslang Road and at Eastfield branch left into Main Street and follow through Burnhill Street and Westmuir Place into Prospecthill Road. Turn left into Aikenhead Road and right into Mount Annan for Kinghorn Drive and the Stadium; From the South: Take the A77 Fenwick Road, through Kilmarnock Road into Pollokshaws Road then turn right into Langside Avenue. Pass through Battle Place to Battlefield Road and turn left into Cathcart Road. Turn right into Letherby Drive, right into Carmunnock Road and 1st left into Mount Annan Drive for the Stadium; From the North & East: Exit M8 Junction 15 and passing Infirmary on left proceed into High Street and cross the Albert Bridge into Crown Street. Join Cathcart Road and proceed South until it becomes Carmunnock Road. Turn left into Mount Annan Drive and left again into Kinghorn Drive for the Stadium.

THE F. A. CARLING PREMIERSHIP

Founded

1992

Address

16 Lancaster Gate, London   W2 3LW

Phone

(0171) 402-7151

THE ENDSLEIGH INSURANCE FOOTBALL LEAGUE

Founded

1888

Address

Lytham St. Annes, Lancashire   FY8 1JG

Phone

(01253) 729421

ARSENAL FC

Founded: 1886
Turned Professional: 1891
Limited Company: 1893
Admitted to League: 1893
Former Name(s): Royal Arsenal (1886-91); Woolwich Arsenal (1891-1914)
Nickname: 'Gunners'
Ground: Arsenal Stadium, Avenell Road, Highbury, London   N5 1BU

Record Attendance: 73,295 (9/3/35)
Colours: Shirts - Red with White Sleeves
Shorts - White
Telephone No.: (0171) 226-0304
Ticket Office: (0171) 354-5404
Pitch Size: 110 × 71yds
Ground Capacity: 38,500 (All seats)

GENERAL INFORMATION

Supporters Club Administrator: Barry Baker
Address: 154 St. Thomas's Road, Finsbury Park, London   N4
Telephone Number: (0171) 226-1627
Car Parking: Street Parking
Coach Parking: Drayton Park (N5)
Nearest Railway Station: Drayton Park/ Finsbury Park
Nearest Tube Station: Arsenal (Piccadilly) Adjacent
Club Shop:
Opening Times: Weekdays 9.30-5.00
Sat. Matchdays 1.00pm onwards
Telephone No.: (0171) 226-9562
Postal Sales: Yes
Nearest Police Station: 284 Hornsey Road, Holloway
Police Force: Metropolitan
Police Telephone No.: (0171) 263-9090

GROUND INFORMATION

Away Supporters' Entrances: South Stand
Away Supporters' Sections: South Stand - Blocks 17 & 18
Family Facilities: **Location of Stand**: West Stand
Capacity of Stand: 2,000

ADMISSION INFO (1995/96 PRICES)

Adult Seating: £11.00 - £25.00
Child Seating: £5.00 - £5.50 (members only) - in Family Stand
Programme Price: £1.50
FAX Number: (0171) 226-0329

WEST STAND
Highbury Hill Turnstiles

SOUTH STAND

NORTH BANK STAND (GILLESPIE ROAD)

EAST STAND
AVENELL ROAD   BUS

Travelling Supporters Information:
Routes: From North: Exit M1 junction 2 following City signs. After Holloway Road Station (6.25 miles) 3rd left into Drayton Park, after 0.75 mile right into Aubert Park and 2nd left into Avenell Road. From South: From London Bridge follow signs to Bank of England then Angel. Right at Traffic-lights to Highbury Roundabout (1 mile), into Holloway Road then 3rd right into Drayton Park (then as North). From West: Exit M4 Junction 1 towards Chiswick (A315), left after 1 mile (A40) to M41 the A40(M) to A501 Ring Road turn left at Angel to Highbury Roundabout (then as South).

ASTON VILLA FC

Founded: 1874	**Record Attendance**: 76,588 (2/3/46)
Turned Professional: 1885	**Colours**: Shirts - Claret w/ Narrow Blue Stripe
Limited Company: 1896	Shorts - White
Admitted to League: 1888 (Founder)	**Telephone No.**: (0121) 327-2299
Former Name(s): None	**Ticket Office**: (0121) 327-5353
Nickname: 'The Villans'; 'Villa'	**Pitch Size**: 115 × 75yds
Ground: Villa Park, Trinity Road,	**Ground Capacity**: 40,100 (All Seats)
Birmingham B6 6HE	

GENERAL INFORMATION

Supporters Club Administrator: -
Address: c/o Club's Commercial Dept.
Telephone Number: (0121) 327-5399
Car Parking: Aston Villa Leisure Centre Car Park, Aston Hall Rd.
Coach Parking: Opposite ground
Nearest Railway Station: Witton or Aston (5 minutes walk)
Nearest Bus Station: Birmingham Centre
Bus Services to Ground: 7/11/440
Club Shop:
Opening Times: Weekdays/Matchdays 9.30-5.00 (Closes for Match)
Telephone No.: (0121) 327-2800
Postal Sales: Yes
Nearest Police Station: Queen's Road, Aston (0.5 mile)
Police Force: West Midlands
Police Telephone No.: (0121) 322-6010

GROUND INFORMATION

Away Supporters' Entrances: All Seating - Witton End - R Block/Doug Ellis Stand - Lower Q Block
Away Supporters' Sections: Witton End - R Block
Family Facilities: Location of Stand: North Stand
Capacity of Stand: 3,940

ADMISSION INFO (1995/96 PRICES)

Adult Seating: £12.00 to £14.00
Child Seating: £5.00 to £8.00
Programme Price: £1.20
FAX Number: (0121) 322-2107

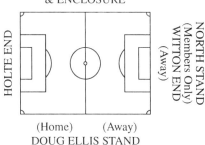

TRINITY ROAD STAND & ENCLOSURE

HOLTE END

NORTH STAND (Members Only) (Away)
WITTON END

(Home)   (Away)
DOUG ELLIS STAND

⇒ BUS →

Travelling Supporters Information:
Routes: From all parts: Exit M6 Junction 6 (Spaghetti Junction). Follow signs Birmingham (NE). 3rd Exit at Roundabout and in 0.5 mile, right into Aston Hall Road.
Bus Services: Service 7 from Corporation Street to Witton Square, also specials.

11

BARNET FC

Founded: 1888	**Record Attendance**: 11,026 (1952)
Turned Professional: 1891	**Colours**: Shirts - Amber with Black Collar
Limited Company: 1893	Shorts - Black + Amber Trim
Admitted to League: 1991	**Telephone No.**: (0181) 441-6932
Former Name(s): Barnet Alston	**Ticket Office**: (0181) 441-6932
Nickname: 'Bees'	**Pitch Size**: 113 × 72yds
Ground: Underhill Stadium, Westcombe	**Ground Capacity**: 3,924
Drive, Barnet, Herts. EN5 2BE	**Seating Capacity**: 987

GENERAL INFORMATION
Supporters Club Administrator: c/o Club Shop
Address: c/o Club Shop
Telephone Number: -
Car Parking: Street Parking/ High Barnet Underground Car park
Coach Parking: By Police Direction
Nearest Railway Station: New Barnet (1.5 miles)
Nearest Tube Station: High Barnet (Northern) 5 mins.
Club Shop:
Opening Times: Monday-Friday & Saturday Matchdays 9.00am to 7.00pm
Telephone No.: (0181) 364-9601
Postal Sales: Yes
Nearest Police Station: Barnet (0.25 mile)
Police Force: Metropolitan
Police Telephone No.: (0181) 200-2212

GROUND INFORMATION
Away Supporters' Entrances: Priory Grove
Away Supporters' Sections: South Terrace
Family Facilities: **Location of Stand**: Family Stand
Capacity of Stand: 200
ADMISSION INFO (1995/96 PRICES)
Adult Standing: £6.00 & £7.00
Adult Seating: £12.00 (£10 in Family Stand)
Child Standing: £3.50
Child Seating: £6.00 (£5 in Family Stand)
Programme Price: £1.20
FAX Number: (0181) 447-0655
(Family Tickets are available)
Note: Concessionary prices available to members only.

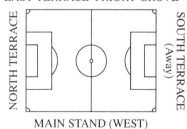

EAST TERRACE PRIORY GROVE

NORTH TERRACE

SOUTH TERRACE (Away)

MAIN STAND (WEST)
BARNET LANE

Travelling Supporters Information:
Routes: The ground is situated off the Great North Road (A1000) at the foot of Barnet Hill near to the junction with Station Road (A110). Barnet Lane is on to the West of the A1000 next to the Cricket ground.

BARNSLEY FC

Founded: 1887	**Record Attendance**: 40,255 (15/2/36)
Turned Professional: 1888	**Colours**: Shirts - Red
Limited Company: 1899	Shorts - White
Admitted to League: 1898	**Telephone No.**: (01226) 295353
Former Name(s): Barnsley St.Peter's	**Ticket Office**: (01226) 295353
Nickname: 'Tykes'; 'Colliers'; 'Reds'	**Pitch Size**: 110 × 75yds
Ground: Oakwell Ground, Grove Street, Barnsley, S71 1ET	**Ground Capacity**: 19,034 (All Seats)

GENERAL INFORMATION
Supporters Club Chairman: Mr. A. Bloore
Address: c/o Barnsley F.C., Oakwell Ground, Barnsley, S71 1ET
Telephone Number: (01302) 883481
Car Parking: Queen's Ground Car Park (adjacent)
Coach Parking: Queen's Ground Car Park
Nearest Railway Station: Barnsley Exchange (5 minutes walk)
Nearest Bus Station: Barnsley Exchange
Club Shop:
Opening Times: Weekdays 9.00-5.00 Saturday Matchdays 9.00-5.30; Saturdays with no home Matches 9.00-12.00
Telephone No.: (01226) 295353
Postal Sales: Yes (Also Credit Card sales)
Nearest Police Station: Churchfields, Barnsley
Police Force: South Yorkshire
Police Telephone No.: (01226) 206161

GROUND INFORMATION
Away Supporters' Entrances: West Stand & Spion Kop (Open)
Away Supporters' Sections: West Stand
Family Facilities:
Accommodated throughout the Ground

ADMISSION INFO (1995/96 PRICES)
Adult Seating: £10.00 - £12.00
Child Seating: £5.50 - £6.00
Programme Price: £1.30
FAX Number: (01226) 201000
Note: Concessions do not always apply to Away fans.

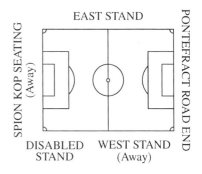

Travelling Supporters Information:
Routes: From All Parts: Exit M1 Junction 37 and follow 'Football Ground' signs to ground (2 miles).

BIRMINGHAM CITY FC

Founded: 1875
Turned Professional: 1885
Limited Company: 1888
Admitted to League: 1892
Former Name(s): Small Heath Alliance FC
(1875-88); Small Heath FC (1888-1905);
Birmingham FC (1905-1945)
Nickname: 'Blues'
Ground: St. Andrew's, St. Andrew's Street,
Birmingham B9 4NH

Record Attendance: 68,844 (11/2/39)
Colours: Shirts - Blue
        Shorts - Blue
Telephone No.: (0121) 772-0101
Ticket Office: (0121) 766-5743/753-3408
Pitch Size: 115 × 75yds
Ground Capacity: 25,000 (All Seats)

GENERAL INFORMATION
Supp. Club Administrator: Linda Goodman
Address: 69 Malmesbury Road, Small
Heath, Birmingham
Telephone Number: (0121) 773-5088
Car Parking: Street Parking
Coach Parking: Coventry Road
Nearest Railway Station: Birmingham New
Street or Birmingham Moor St. (20 mins walk)
Nearest Bus Station: Digbeth
Bus Services to Ground: 96 / 97 / 99 / 15 /
17 /58 / 60 / 900
Club Shops: Dale End & Cattel Road
Opening Times: Monday to Saturday 9.00am
to 5.30pm (7.00pm on Thursdays).
Telephone No.: (0121) 753-1997
Postal Sales: Yes
Nearest Police Station:Bordesley Green
(0.5 mile)
Police Force: West Midlands
Police Telephone No.: (0121) 772-1166

GROUND INFORMATION
Away Supporters' Entrances: Railway Paddock
Away Supporters' Sections: Railway Paddock
Family Facilities: Location of Stand:
Kop Family Stand
Capacity of Stand: 1,800

ADMISSION INFO (1995/96 PRICES)
Adult Seating: £6.00 - £16.00
Child Seating: £5.00 - £8.00
Programme Price: £1.50
FAX Number: (0121) 766-7866
Note: Prices vary according to match category and
position in ground

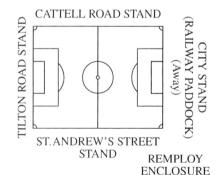

Travelling Supporters Information:
Routes: From All Parts: Exit M6 Junction 6, to A38(M) (Aston Expressway), leave at 2nd exit then 1st exit
at Roundabout along Dartmouth Middleway, after 1.25 miles take left into St. Andrew's Street.
Bus Services: Service 97 from Birmingham: Services 98 & 99 from Digbeth.

BLACKBURN ROVERS FC

Founded: 1875	**Record Attendance**: 61,783 (2/3/29)
Turned Professional: 1880	**Colours**: Shirts - Blue & White Halves
Limited Company: 1897	Shorts - White
Admitted to League: 1888 (Founder)	**Telephone No.**: (01254) 698888
Former Name(s): None	**Ticket Office**: (01254) 696767
Nickname: 'Rovers'; 'Blues & Whites'	**Pitch Size**: 117 × 73yds
Ground: Ewood Park, Blackburn,	**Ground Capacity**: 31,169 (All Seats)
Lancashire, BB2 4JF	

GENERAL INFORMATION
Supporters Club Administrator:
Barbara Magee
Address: c/o Club
Telephone Number: (01254) 698888
Car Parking: Street Parking (nearby)
Coach Parking: By Police direction
Nearest Railway Station: Blackburn
Central (1.5 miles)
Nearest Bus Station: Blackburn Central
(1.5 miles)
Club Shop:
Opening Times: Weekdays 9.00-5.00
Saturday Matchdays 9.30-5.00
Telephone No.: (01254) 672137
Postal Sales: Yes
Nearest Police Station: Blackburn (2 miles)
Police Force: Lancashire
Police Telephone No.: (01254) 51212

GROUND INFORMATION
Away Supporters' Entrances: Darwen End
Away Supporters' Sections: Darwen End
Family Facilities: Location of Stand:
Blackburn End - Upper Tier
Capacity of Stand: 3,000
ADMISSION INFO (1995/96 PRICES)
Adult Seating: £14.00 - £17.50
Child Seating: £7.00 - £8.00
Programme Price: £1.30
FAX Number: (01254) 671042

WALKERSTEEL STAND

KIDDER STREET

BLACKBURN END

DARWEN END (Away)

JACK WALKER STAND
BOLTON ROAD

Travelling Supporters Information:
Routes: From North, South and West: Exit M6 Junction 31, or take A666, follow signs for Blackburn then for Bolton Road, after 1.5 miles turn left into Kidder Street.; From East: Use A679 or A677 and follow signs for Bolton Road (then as above).

BLACKPOOL FC

Founded: 1887	**Record Attendance**: 38,098 (17/9/55)
Turned Professional: 1887	**Colours**: Shirts - Tangerine
Limited Company: 1896	Shorts - White
Admitted to League: 1896	**Telephone No.**: (01253) 404331
Former Name(s): Merged with Blackpool	**Ticket Office**: (01253) 404331
St.Johns 1887	**Pitch Size**: 112 × 74yds
Nickname: 'Seasiders'	**Ground Capacity**: 9,701
Ground: Bloomfield Road, Blackpool	**Seating Capacity**: 2,987
Lancashire, FY1 6JJ	

GENERAL INFORMATION

Supporters Club Administrator: Colin Johnson
Address: Blackpool Supporters' Club, Bloomfield Road, Blackpool
Telephone Number: (01253) 46428 (evenings only 7pm-11pm)
Car Parking: Car Park at Ground (3,000 cars) and Street Parking
Coach Parking: Mecca Car Park (behind Spion Kop)
Nearest Railway Station: Blackpool South (5 minutes walk)
Nearest Bus Station: Talbot Road (2 miles)
Club Shop:
Opening Times: Daily 9.00-5.30
Telephone No.: (01253) 404331
Postal Sales: Yes
Nearest Police Station: South Shore, Montague Street, Blackpool
Police Force: Lancashire
Police Telephone No.: (01253) 293933

GROUND INFORMATION

Away Supporters' Entrances: Spion Kop Turnstiles
Away Supporters' Sections: Spion Kop (Open) & East Paddock North Section (Covered)
Family Facilities: Location of Stand:
West Stand (South End)
Capacity of Stand: 400 (Family area)

ADMISSION INFO (1995/96 PRICES)

Adult Standing: £7.50
Adult Seating: £9.00 - £9.50
Child Standing: £4.00
Child Seating: £5.50 - £6.00
Programme Price: £1.20
FAX Number: (01253) 405011
FAMILY BLOCK: - Various additional discounts
1 Adult + 1 Child £10.50
2 Adults + 1 Child £18.00

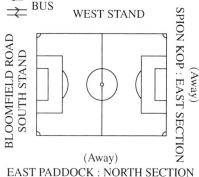

Travelling Supporters Information:
Routes: From All Parts: Exit M6 Junction 32 to M55. Follow signs for main car parks along new 'spine' road to car parks at side of ground.

BOLTON WANDERERS FC

Founded: 1874	**Record Attendance**: 69,912 (18/2/33)
Turned Professional: 1880	**Colours**: Shirts - White
Limited Company: 1895	Shorts - Blue
Admitted to League: 1888 (Founder)	**Telephone No.**: (01204) 389200
Former Name(s): Christchurch FC (1874-77)	**Ticket Office**: (01204) 521101
Nickname: 'Trotters'	**Pitch Size**: 113 × 75yds
Ground: Burnden Park, Manchester Road,	**Ground Capacity**: 20,800 (Approximately)
Bolton BL3 2QR	**Seating Capacity**: 7,850

GENERAL INFORMATION
Supporters Club Administrator:
P. Entwistle
Address: 21 Woodfield, Bolton
Telephone Number: -
Car Parking: Rosehill Car Park (Nearby)
Coach Parking: Rosehill Car Park
Manchester Road
Nearest Railway Station: Bolton Trinity
Street (0.5 mile)
Nearest Bus Station: Moor Lane, Bolton
Club Shop:
Opening Times: Daily 9.30-5.30
Telephone No.: (01204) 389200
Postal Sales: Yes
Nearest Police Station: Howell Croft, Bolton
Police Force: Greater Manchester
Police Telephone No.: (01204) 522466

GROUND INFORMATION
Away Supporters' Entrances: Embankment
Turnstiles
Away Supporters' Sections: Embankment (Open -
No Seating)
Family Facilities: **Location of Stand**:
Great Lever Stand
Capacity of Stand: 3,000

ADMISSION INFO (1995/96 PRICES)
Adult Standing: £11.00
Adult Seating: Season tickets only
Child Standing: £8.00
Child Seating: Season tickets only
Programme Price: £1.50
FAX Number: (01204) 382334

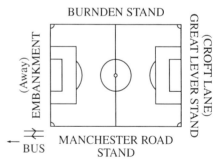

Travelling Supporters Information:
Routes: From North: Exit M61 Junction 5 or use A666 or A676. Follow signs for Farnworth (B653) into Manchester Road. After 0.5 mile turn left into Croft Lane; From South, East and West: Exit M62 Junction 14 to M61, after 2 miles leave motorway then 1st exit at Roundabout (B6536). After 2 miles turn right into Croft Lane.

AFC BOURNEMOUTH

Founded: 1890	**Record Attendance**: 28,799 (2/3/57)
Turned Professional: 1912	**Colours**: Shirts - Red and Black Stripes
Limited Company: 1914	Shorts - Black
Admitted to League: 1923	**Telephone No.**: (01202) 395381
Former Name(s): Boscombe St.Johns FC	**Ticket Office**: (01202) 395381
(1890-99); Boscombe FC (1899-1923)	**Pitch Size**: 112 × 75yds
Bournemouth & Boscombe Ath. FC (1923-72)	**Ground Capacity**: 11,880
Nickname: 'Cherries'	**Seating Capacity**: 3,130
Ground: Dean Court, Bournemouth, Dorset	BH7 7AF

GENERAL INFORMATION
Supporters Club Administrator: -
Address: Dean Court Supporters' Club
Bournemouth BH7 7AF
Telephone Number: (01202) 398313
Car Parking: Car Park (1500 cars) Behind
Main Stand
Coach Parking: Kings Park (Nearby)
Nearest Railway Station: Bournemouth
Central (1.5 miles)
Nearest Bus Station: Holdenhurst Road,
Bournemouth
Club Shop:
Opening Times: Weekdays 9.00-5.00
Saturday Matchdays 1.00pm to Kick-off
Closed on Wednesdays
Telephone No.: (01202) 397777/395381
Postal Sales: Yes
Nearest Police Station: Boscombe (400 yds)
Police Force: Dorset
Police Telephone No.: (01202) 552099

GROUND INFORMATION
Away Supporters' Entrances: Main Stand Turnstiles
(Block A)
Away Supporters' Sections: Brighton Beach Terrace
(Open)
Family Room and Enclosure:
Family Block (Main Stand - F Block)
Capacity of Stand: 700

ADMISSION INFO (1995/96 PRICES)
Adult Standing: £7.50
Adult Seating: £8.50 - £11.50
Child Standing: £4.00
Child Seating: £4.50 - £6.50
Programme Price: £1.20
FAX Number: (0202) 309797

Travelling Supporters Information:
Routes: From North & East: Take A338 into Bournemouth and turn left at 'Kings Park' turning. Then first left at mini-roundabout and first right into Thistlebarrow Road for Ground. From West: Use A3049, turning right at Wallisdown Roundabout to Talbot Roundabout. Take first exit at Talbot Roundabout (over Wessex Way), then left at mini-roundabout. Go straight across traffic lights then right at mini-roundabout into Kings Park for ground.
Bus Services: Service 25 passes ground.

BRADFORD CITY FC

Founded: 1903
Turned Professional: 1903
Limited Company: 1908 (Reformed 1983)
Admitted to League: 1903
Former Name(s): None
Nickname: 'Bantams'
Ground: The Pulse Stadium, Valley Parade, Bradford   BD8 7DY

Record Attendance: 39,146 (11/3/11)
Colours: Shirts - Claret & Amber
Shorts - Black
Telephone No.: (01274) 306062
Ticket Office: (01274) 306062
Pitch Size: 110 × 80yds
Ground Capacity: 14,810
Seating Capacity: 6,500

GENERAL INFORMATION
Supporters Club Administrator:
Mrs J. Calvert
Address: 1 Westmoor Avenue, Baildon BD17 5HG
Telephone Number: (01274) 591947
Car Parking: Street Parking and car parks (£2.50 entry charge)
Coach Parking: By Police direction
Nearest Railway Station: Bradford Interchange (1 mile)
Nearest Bus Station: Bradford Interchange
Club Shop: Yes
Opening Times: Monday to Saturday 9.00am-5.00pm
Telephone No.: (01274) 306062
Postal Sales: Yes
Nearest Police Station: Tyrrells, Bradford
Police Force: West Yorkshire
Police Telephone No.: (01274) 723422

GROUND INFORMATION
Away Supporters' Entrances: Midland Road
Away Supporters' Sections: Midland Road Standing
Family Facilities: Location of Stand:
N & P Stand
Capacity of Stand: 800 seated

ADMISSION INFO (1995/96 PRICES)
Adult Standing: £7.00
Adult Seating: £11.00
Child Standing: £1.00
Child Seating: £2.00 or £3.00 in the Family Stand
Programme Price: £1.20
FAX Number: (01274) 307457

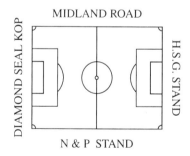

Travelling Supporters Information:
Routes: From North: Take A650 and follow signs for Bradford. A third of a mile after junction with Ring Road turn left into Valley Parade. From East, South and West: Take M62 and exit Junction 26 onto M606. At end take 2nd left from roundabout and onto A6177 Ring Road. At next roundabout (3rd exit) turn right to City Centre (A614). At second roundabout turn right onto Central Ring Road (A6181) then left at next roundabout and left again at following roundabout marked 'Local Access Only'. Pass through traffic lights at the top of the hill following Keighley (A650) sign. Ground is then 0.5 mile along on the right.

BRENTFORD FC

Founded: 1889	**Record Attendance**: 39,626 (5/3/38)
Turned Professional: 1899	**Colours**: Shirts - Red and White Stripes
Limited Company: 1901	Shorts - Black
Admitted to League: 1920	**Telephone No.**: (0181) 847-2511
Former Name(s): None	**Ticket Office**: (0181) 847-2511
Nickname: 'Bees'	**Pitch Size**: 111 × 74yds
Ground: Griffin Park, Braemar Road,	**Ground Capacity**: 13,870
Brentford, Middlesex TW8 0NT	**Seating Capacity**: 4,000

GENERAL INFORMATION
Supporters Club Administrator:
Mr. P. Gilham
Address: 16 Hartland Road, Hampton Hill
Middlesex
Telephone Number: (0181) 941-0425
Car Parking: Street Parking
Coach Parking: Layton Road Car Park
Nearest Railway Station: Brentford Central
(0.5 mile)
Nearest Tube Station: South Ealing
(Piccadilly) (1 mile)
Club Shop:
Opening Times: Monday-Friday 10.00-4.00
& also Matchdays
Telephone No.: (0181) 560-9836
Postal Sales: Yes
Nearest Police Station: Brentford
Police Force: Metropolitan
Police Telephone No.: (0181) 569-9728

GROUND INFORMATION
Away Supporters' Entrances: Brook Road
Away Supporters' Sections: Brook Road - Seats &
Terracing (Covered)
Family Facilities: Location of Stand:
Braemar Road - 'A' Block
Capacity of Stand: 640

ADMISSION INFO (1994/95 PRICES)
Adult Standing: £6.80 Member   £7.80 Non-member
Adult Seating: £8.80 - £12.00 Member
£9.80 - £13.00 Non-member
Child Standing: £4.50 Member   £5.50 Non-member
Child Seating: £6.50 - £9.70 Member
£7.50 - £10.70 Non-member
Programme Price: £1.50
FAX Number: (081) 568-9940

Travelling Supporters Information:
Routes: From North: Take A406 North Circular (from M1/A1) to Chiswick Roundabout and then along the
Great West Road and turn right at the third set of Traffic lights into Ealing Road. From East: Take the A406
to the Chiswick Roundabout, then as North. From West: Exit M4 Junction 2 - down to the Chiswick Round-
about, then as North. From South: Use the A3, M3, A240 or A316 to Kew Road, continue along over Kew
Bridge, then right at the next traffic lights into Ealing Road.

BRIGHTON & HOVE ALBION FC

Founded: 1900
Turned Professional: 1900
Limited Company: 1904
Admitted to League: 1920
Former Name(s): Brighton & Hove Rangers FC (1900-01)
Nickname: 'Seagulls'
Ground: Goldstone Ground, Newtown Road, Hove, Sussex, BN3 7DE

Record Attendance: 36,747 (27/12/58)
Colours: Shirts - Blue & White Stripes
Shorts - Blue
Telephone No.: (01273) 778855
Ticket Office: (01273) 778855
Pitch Size: 111 × 74yds
Ground Capacity: 16,254
Seating Capacity: 5,110

GENERAL INFORMATION
Supporters Club Administrator: Liz Costa
Address: 72 Stoneham Road, Hove BN3 5HH
Telephone Number: (01273) 778855
Car Parking: Greyhound Stadium and street parking
Coach Parking: Conway Street, Hove
Nearest Railway Station: Hove (5 minutes walk)
Nearest Bus Station: Brighton Pool Valley
Club Shop: The Albion Shop, Newtown Rd.
Opening Times: Weekdays 10.00-4.00
Telephone No.: (01273) 778855
Postal Sales: Yes
Nearest Police Station: Hove (1 mile)
Police Force: Sussex
Police Telephone No.: (01273) 778922

GROUND INFORMATION
Away Supporters' Entrances: Goldstone Lane Turnstiles
Away Supporters' Sections: South East Corner (Open Terrace); South Stand (Seats)
Family Facilities: Location of Stand: South Stand - Entrance Newtown Road
Capacity of Stand: 1,500

ADMISSION INFO (1995/96 PRICES)
Adult Standing: £7.00
Adult Seating: West Stand £12.00; South Stand £9.00
Child Standing: £3.50
Child Seating: West Stand £6.00; South Stand £4.50
Programme Price: £1.50
FAX Number: (01273) 321095

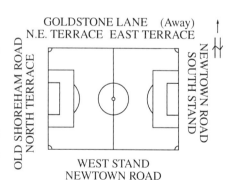

Travelling Supporters Information:
Routes: From North: Take A23, turn right 2 miles after Pyecombe follow Hove signs for 1mile, bear left into Nevill Road (A2023), then turn left at Crossroads (1 mile), into Old Shoreham Road. From East: Take A27 to Brighton then follow Worthing signs into Old Shoreham Road. From West: Take A27 straight into Old Shoreham Road.
Bus Services: Service 11 passes ground.

BRISTOL CITY FC

Founded: 1894	**Record Attendance**: 43,335 (16/2/35)
Turned Professional: 1897	**Colours**: Shirts - Red
Limited Company: 1897	Shorts - White
Admitted to League: 1901	**Telephone No.**: (0117) 963-2812
Former Name(s): Bristol South End FC	**Ticket Office**: (0117) 963-2812
(1894-7)	**Pitch Size**: 115 × 75yds
Nickname: 'Robins'	**Ground Capacity**: 19,815 (All Seats)
Ground: Ashton Gate, Winterstoke Road,	
Ashton Road, Bristol BS3 2EJ	

GENERAL INFORMATION
Supporters Club Administrator:
Mr. G. Williams
Address: c/o Club
Telephone Number: (0117) 966-5554
Car Parking: Street Parking
Coach Parking: Winterstoke Road
Nearest Railway Station: Bristol Temple
Meads (1.5 miles)
Nearest Bus Station: Bristol City Centre
Club Shop:
Opening Times: Weekdays 9.00am - 5.00pm
& Saturdays 9.30am - 12.30am
Telephone No.: (0117) 953-8566
Postal Sales: Yes
Nearest Police Station: Kings Mead Lane
(2 miles) - Office at ground
Police Force: Avon/Somerset
Police Telephone No.: (0117) 927-7777

GROUND INFORMATION
Away Supporters' Entrances: Winterstoke Road
Away Supporters' Sections: Winterstoke Road -
Covered Area
Family Facilities: Location of Stand:
Dolman Stand
Capacity of Stand: 4,741
ADMISSION INFO (1995/96 PRICES)
Adult Seating: £8.50 - £11.00 (See note below)
Child Seating: £4.00 - £7.50
Programme Price: £1.30
FAX Number: (0117) 963-9574

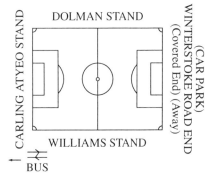

Travelling Supporters Information:
Routes: From North & West: Exit M5 Junction 16, take A38 to Bristol City Centre and follow A38 Taunton signs. Cross Swing Bridge (1.25 miles) and bear left into Winterstoke Road. From East: Take M4 then M32 follow signs to city centre (then as North & West). From South: Exit M5 Junction 18 and follow Taunton signs over Swing Bridge (then as above).
Bus Services: Services 27A & 28A from Railway Station.

BRISTOL ROVERS FC

Founded: 1883
Turned Professional: 1897
Limited Company: 1896
Admitted to League: 1920
Former Name(s): Black Arabs FC (1883-84)
Eastville Rovers FC (1884-96)
Bristol Eastville Rovers FC (1896-7)
Nickname: 'Pirates'; 'Rovers'
Ground: Twerton Park, Bath, Avon

Record Attendance: 18,000
Colours: Shirts - Blue & White Quarters
Shorts - White
Telephone No.: (0117) 986-9999
Ticket Office: (0117) 986-9999
Pitch Size: 110 × 76yds
Ground Capacity: 8,943
Seating Capacity: 1,006
Office: Avonfields House, Somerdale,
Keynsham, Bristol, BS18 2DJ

GENERAL INFORMATION
Supporters Club Administrator:
Mr. Steve Burns
Address: 199 Two Mile Hill Road,
Kingswood BS15 7AZ
Telephone Number: (0117) 961-1772
Car Parking: Very little space at ground -
(permit holders only)
Coach Parking: Avon Street, Bath
Nearest Railway Station: Bath Spa
(1.5 miles)
Nearest Bus Station: Avon Street, Bath
Club Shop:
Opening Times: Weekdays (Club Offices)
9.00am - 5.00pm
Telephone No.: (0117) 986-9999
Postal Sales: Yes
Nearest Police Station: Bath (1.5 miles)
Police Force: Avon & Somerset
Police Telephone No.: (01225) 842439

GROUND INFORMATION
Away Supporters' Entrances: Turnstiles 20/21
Away Supporters' Sections: Bristol End
Family Facilities: Location of Stand:
Family Enclosure Terrace - Bristol End
New Family Stand at side of Main Stand
Capacity of Stand: 236

ADMISSION INFO (1995/96 PRICES)
Adult Standing: £8.00
Adult Seating: £13.00 Main Stand £10 Family Stand
Child Standing: £4.00
Child Seating: £8.50 Main Stand £7 Family Stand
Away Fans: £8.00 - no concessions
Programme Price: £1.30
FAX Number: (0117) 935-3477
Family Enclosure: Adults £7.00 OAP's £4.00
Children £1.00

Travelling Supporters Information:
Routes: Take the A36 into Bath City Centre. Follow along Pulteney Road, then right into Claverton Street and along Lower Bristol Road (A36). Left under Railway (1.5 miles) into Twerton High Street and ground on left.

BURNLEY FC

Founded: 1882
Turned Professional: 1883
Limited Company: 1897
Admitted to League: 1888 (Founder)
Former Name(s): Burnley Rovers FC
Nickname: 'Clarets'
Ground: Turf Moor, Brunshaw Road, Burnley, Lancs. BB10 4BX

Record Attendance: 54,775 (23/2/24)
Colours: Shirts - Claret with Blue Sleeves
Shorts - White
Telephone No.: (01282) 427777
Ticket Office: (01282) 427777
Pitch Size: 114 × 72yds
Ground Capacity: 21,290
Seating Capacity: 7,326

GENERAL INFORMATION
Supporters Club Administrator: David Spencer
Address: c/o Club
Telephone Number: (01282) 435176
Car Parking: Ormerod Road, adjacent to Fire Station (2 mins. walk) & Fulledge Recreation Ground (2 minutes walk)
Coach Parking: By Police direction
Nearest Railway Station: Burnley Central (1.5 miles)
Nearest Bus Station: Burnley (5 mins. walk)
Club Shop:
Opening Times: 9.15-5.00 Mondays - Saturday Matchdays. Friday Evenings 5-7pm Saturdays (no match) 9.15 - 1.00pm
Telephone No.: (01282) 427777
Postal Sales: Yes
Nearest Police Station: Parker Lane, Burnley (5 minutes walk)
Police Force: Lancashire Constabulary
Police Telephone No.: (01282) 425001

GROUND INFORMATION
Away Supporters' Entrances: Belvedere Road Endsleigh Stand (Seats) & Sanderson Ford Stand
Away Supporters' Sections: Covered Terracing
Family Facilities: Location of Stand: Endsleigh Stand (Members Only)
Capacity of Stand: 4,166
Away Families: Community programme & visiting Junior Supporters Clubs

ADMISSION INFO (1995/96 PRICES)
Adult Standing: £7.00 to £7.50
Adult Seating: £9.50 to £11.50
Child Standing: £3.50 to £4.00
Child Seating: £4.50 to £6.00
Programme Price: £1.50
FAX Number: (01282) 428938

SANDERSON FORD STAND
COVERED TERRACING
(Away)

BELVEDERE ROAD
ENDSLEIGH STAND
(Away)

BEE HOLE LANE

BOB LORD STAND
BRUNSHAW ROAD

BUS

Travelling Supporters Information:
Routes: From North: Follow A682 to Town Centre and take first exit at roundabout (Ritzy Nightclub) into Yorkshire Street. Follow through traffic signals into Brunshaw Road. From East: Follow A646 to A671 then along Todmorden Road towards Town Centre. At traffic signals (crossroads) turn right into Brunshaw Road. From West & South: Exit M6 at Junction 31 and take A59 and then A677 towards Blackburn. Then follow A6119 (Blackburn ring road) to M65. Take M65 to Junction 10 and follow signs for Town Centre. At roundabout in centre take third exit into Yorkshire Street. Then as North.

BURY FC

Founded: 1885	**Record Attendance**: 35,000 (9/1/60)
Turned Professional: 1885	**Colours**: Shirts - White
Limited Company: 1897	Shorts - Royal Blue
Admitted to League: 1894	**Telephone No.**: (0161) 764-7674
Former Name(s): None	**Ticket Office**: (0161) 764-4881
Nickname: 'Shakers'	**Pitch Size**: 112 × 72yds
Ground: Gigg Lane, Bury, Lancs. BL9 9HR	**Ground Capacity**: 8,700 (All Seats) (Rising to 12,200 during the Season)

GENERAL INFORMATION

Supporters Club Administrator: P. Cullen
Address: c/o Club
Car Parking: Street Parking
Coach Parking: By Police Direction
Nearest Railway Station: Bury Interchange (1 mile)
Nearest Bus Station: Bury Interchange
Club Shop:
Opening Times: Daily 9.00-5.00
Telephone No.: (0161) 705-2144
Postal Sales: Yes (Price lists available)
Nearest Police Station: Irwell Street, Bury
Police Force: Greater Manchester
Police Telephone No.: (0161) 872-5050

GROUND INFORMATION

Away Supporters' Entrances: Gigg Lane
Away Supporters' Sections: Main Stand
Family Facilities: Location of Stand:
Family Stand - Ron Wood Stand
Capacity of Stand: 1,800

ADMISSION INFO (1995/96 PRICES)

Adult Seating: £8.00 - £10.00 (£6 - £8 Members)
Child Seating: £4.00 - £5.00 (£3 - £4 Members)
Programme Price: £1.20
FAX Number: (0161) 764-5521 & (0161) 763-3103

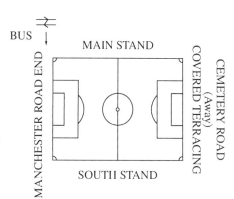

Travelling Supporters Information:
Routes: From North: Exit M66 Junction 2, take Bury Road (A58) for 0.5 mile, then turn left into Heywood Street and follow this into Parkhills Road until its end, turn left into Manchester Road (A56) then left into Gigg Lane. From South, East & West: Exit M62 Junction 17, take Bury Road (A56) for 3 miles then turn right into Gigg Lane.

CAMBRIDGE UNITED FC

Founded: 1919	**Record Attendance**: 14,000 (1/5/70)
Turned Professional: 1946	**Colours**: Shirts - Amber
Limited Company: 1948	Shorts - Black
Admitted to League: 1970	**Telephone No.**: (01223) 566500
Former Name(s): Abbey United FC (1919-49)	**Ticket Office**: (01223) 566500
Nickname: 'U's'; 'United'	**Pitch Size**: 110 × 74yds
Ground: Abbey Stadium, Newmarket Road	**Ground Capacity**: 9,667
Cambridge CB5 8LN	**Seating Capacity**: 3,265

GENERAL INFORMATION

Supporters Club Administrator: -
Address: c/o Club
Telephone Number: -
Car Parking: Coldhams Common (Do not park in the sidestreets)
Coach Parking: Coldhams Common
Nearest Railway Station: Cambridge (2mls)
Nearest Bus Station: Cambridge City Centre
Club Shop:
Opening Times: Weekdays 10.00-5.00 & Matchdays
Telephone No.: (01223) 566503
Postal Sales: Yes
Nearest Police Station:Parkside, Cambridge
Police Force: Cambridgeshire
Police Telephone No.: (01223) 358966

GROUND INFORMATION

Away Supporters' Entrances: Coldham Common - Turnstiles 20-23
Away Supporters' Sections: South Terrace (part covered - 360 seats/1,900 standing)
Family Facilities: Location of Stand:
Main Stand
Capacity of Stand: 300

ADMISSION INFO (1995/96 PRICES)

Adult Standing: £7.00
Adult Seating: £7.00 - £12.00
Child Standing: £4.00
Child Seating: £4.00 - £6.00
Programme Price: £1.20
FAX Number: (0223) 566502

Travelling Supporters Information:
Routes: From North: Take A1 and A604 into City Centre, then take the A45. Turn off the A45 onto the B1047, sign posted for Cambridge Airport, Horningsea and Fen Ditton. Turn right at the top of the slip road and travel all the way through Fen Ditton. Turn right at the traffic lights at the end of the village. Go straight on at the roundabout onto Newmarket Road. The ground is 500 yards on the left. From the South and East: Take the A10 or A130 into Cambridge and join the A45. Then as North. From West: Take A422 to Cambridge and join the A45. Then as North.
Bus Services: Services 180 & 181 from Railway Station to City Centre/ 182 & 183 to Ground.

CARDIFF CITY FC

Founded: 1899	**Record Attendance**: 61,566 (14/10/61)
Turned Professional: 1910	**Colours**: Shirts - Blue
Limited Company: 1910	Shorts - White
Admitted to League: 1920	**Telephone No.**: (01222) 398636
Former Name(s): Riverside FC (1899-1910)	**Ticket Office**: (01222) 398636
Nickname: 'Bluebirds'	**Pitch Size**: 112 × 76yds
Ground: Ninian Park, Sloper Road,	**Ground Capacity**: 21,403
Cardiff, CF1 8SX	**Seating Capacity**: 5,563

GENERAL INFORMATION
Supporters Club Administrator:
Kathy Shea
Address: Equity House, 6/7 Duke Street,
Cardiff CF1 1AY
Telephone Number: (01426) 950267 -
(messages only)
Car Parking: Sloper Road & Street Parking
Coach Parking: Sloper Road (Adjacent)
Nearest Railway Station: Cardiff Central
(1 mile)
Nearest Bus Station: Cardiff Central
Club Shop:
Opening Times: Weekdays 9.00-5.00
& Matchdays 1.5 hours before kick-off
Telephone No.: (01222) 398636
Postal Sales: Yes
Nearest Police Station: Cowbridge Road East
Cardiff (1 mile)
Police Force: South Wales
Police Telephone No.: (01222) 222111

GROUND INFORMATION
Away Supporters' Entrances: Grangetown End,
Sloper Road
Away Supporters' Sections: Grangetown End (Open)
Family Facilities: Location of Stand:
Below Grandstand and Canton Stand
Capacity of Stand: 3,271

ADMISSION INFO (1994/95 PRICES)
Adult Standing: Between £6.00 and £10.00
Adult Seating: Between £6.00 and £12.00
Child Standing: Between £3.00 and £5.00
Child Seating: Between £5.00 and £6.00
Programme Price: £1.00
FAX Number: (01222) 341148

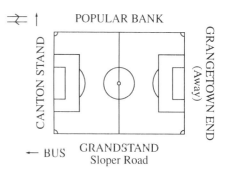

Travelling Supporters Information:
Routes: From All Parts: Exit M4 at Junction 33 and follow Penarth (A4232) Signs. After 6 miles, take the B4267 to Ninian Park.

CARLISLE UNITED FC

Founded: 1903	**Record Attendance**: 27,500 (5/1/57)
Turned Professional: 1903	**Colours**: Shirts - Royal Blue
Limited Company: 1921	Shorts - White
Admitted to League: 1928	**Telephone No.**: (01228) 26237
Former Name(s): Formed by Amalgamation	**Ticket Office**: (01228) 26237
of Shaddongate Utd FC & Carlisle Red Rose FC	**Pitch Size**: 117 × 78yds
Nickname: 'Cumbrians' 'Blues'	**Ground Capacity**: 17,167
Ground: Brunton Park, Warwick Road,	**Seating Capacity**: 8,036
Carlisle CA1 1LL	

GENERAL INFORMATION
Supporters Club Administrator:
M. Hudson
Address: c/o Club
Telephone Number: (01228) 24014
Car Parking: Rear of Ground via St. Aidans Road
Coach Parking: St. Aidans Road Car Park
Nearest Railway Station: Carlisle Citadel (1 mile)
Nearest Bus Station: Lowther Street, Carlisle
Club Shop:
Opening Times: Weekdays 9.00-5.00
Saturday Matchdays 10.00-3.00
Telephone No.: (01228) 24014
Postal Sales: Yes
Nearest Police Station: Rickergate, Carlisle (1.5 miles)
Police Force: Cumbria Constabulary
Police Telephone No.: (01228) 28191

GROUND INFORMATION
Away Supporters' Entrances: Turnstiles 22 to 25
Away Supporters' Sections: Visitors enclosure (Standing only)
Family Facilities: Location of Stand:
Main Stand & East Stand
Capacity of Stand: -

ADMISSION INFO (1995/96 PRICES)
Adult Standing: £7.50
Adult Seating: £9.50 or £11.00
Child Standing: £4.50
Child Seating: £5.50 (In Family Stand)
Programme Price: £1.20
FAX Number: (01228) 30138

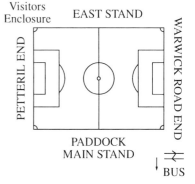

Visitors Enclosure — EAST STAND — PETTERIL END — WARWICK ROAD END — PADDOCK MAIN STAND — BUS

Travelling Supporters Information:
Routes: From North, South & East: Exit M6 Junction 43 and follow signs for Carlisle (A69) into Warwick Road. From West: Take A69 straight into Warwick Road.

28

CHARLTON ATHLETIC FC

Founded: 1905
Turned Professional: 1920
Limited Company: 1984 / PLC 1994
Admitted to League: 1921
Former Name(s): None
Nickname: 'Addicks'
Ground: The Valley, Floyd Road, Charlton
London   SE7 8BL

Record Attendance: 75,031 (12/2/38)
Colours: Shirts - Red
         Shorts - White
Telephone No.: (0181) 293-4567
Ticket Office: (0181) 858-5888
Pitch Size: 112 × 73yds
Ground Capacity: 14,947 (All Seats)

GENERAL INFORMATION
Supporters Club Administrator:
Craig Norris
Address: P.O. Box 387, London   SE9 6EH
Telephone Number: (0181) 304-1593
Car Parking: Street Parking
Coach Parking: By Police Direction
Nearest Railway Station: Charlton (2 mins walk)
Nearest Bus Station:
Club Shop:(0181) 305-1289
Opening Times: Weekdays 10.00-6.00pm
Saturdays 10.00-2.45
Telephone No.: (0181) 293-4567
Postal Sales: Yes
Nearest Police Station: Greenwich (2 miles)
Police Force: Metropolitan
Police Telephone No.: (0181) 853-8212

GROUND INFORMATION
Away Supporters' Entrances: Valley Grove South
Away Supporters' Sections: Valley Grove South
Family Facilities: Location of Stand:
East Stand - Block H
Capacity of Stand: Not specified

ADMISSION INFO (1995/96 PRICES)
Adult Seating: £8.00 or £12.00 Members
               £12.00 or £14.00 Non-Members
Child Seating: £3.00 Members
               £3.00 or £6.00 Non-Members
Programme Price: £1.50
FAX Numbers: (0181) 293-5143 (General Office)
            (0181) 853-4001 (Box Office)

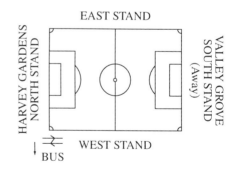

Travelling Supporters Information:
Routes: From All Parts: Exit M25 at Junction 2 (A2 London-bound) and follow until the road becomes A102(M). Take the exit marked Woolwich Ferry and turn right along A206 Woolwich Road. Turn right at the first set of Traffic Lights & Floyd Road is the 2nd turning on the left.

CHELSEA FC

Founded: 1905	**Record Attendance**: 82,905 (12/10/35)
Turned Professional: 1905	**Colours**: Shirts - Blue
Limited Company: 1905	Shorts - Blue
Admitted to League: 1905	**Telephone No.**: (0171) 385-5545
Former Name(s): None	**Credit Card Bookings**: (0171) 386-7799
Nickname: 'Blues'	**Pitch Size**: 114 × 71yds
Ground: Stamford Bridge, Fulham Road, London SW6 1HS	**Ground Capacity**: 27,000 Approximately (All Seats)

GENERAL INFORMATION
Supporters Club Administrator: Pippa Robinson
Address: Contact via Club
Telephone Number: (0171) 385-5545
Car Parking: Street Parking
Coach Parking: By Police Direction
Nearest Railway Station: Fulham Broadway (5 minutes walk)
Nearest Tube Station: Fulham Broadway (District)
Club Shop:
Opening Times: Weekdays 9.00am - 5.00pm & Matchdays
Telephone No.: (0171) 381-4569
FAX No.: (0171) 381-5697
Postal Sales: Yes
Nearest Police Station: Fulham
Police Force: Metropolitan
Police Telephone No.: (0171) 385-1212

GROUND INFORMATION
Away Supporters' Entrances: East Stand
Away Supporters' Sections: East Stand
Family Facilities: Location of Stand: East Stand (North Side)
Capacity of Stand: 2,010

ADMISSION INFO (1995/96 PRICES)
Adult Seating: £10.00 - £35.00: Depending on class of game, place where seated, and whether or not you are members. Also special rates in a Family Section. Phone club for further details.
Child Seating: £5.00 - £6.00
Programme Price: £1.50
FAX Number: (0171) 381-4831

EAST STAND
(Away)

NORTH TERRACE

SOUTH TERRACE

WEST STAND

Travelling Supporters Information:
Routes: From North & East: Follow Central London signs from A1/M1 to Hyde Park Corner, then signs Guildford (A3) to Knightsbridge (A4) after 1 mile turn left into Fulham Road; From South: Take A13 or A24 then A219 to cross Putney Bridge and follow signs 'West End' (A304) to join A308 into Fulham Road; From West: Take M4 then A4 to Central London, then signs to Westminster (A3220). After 0.75 mile turn right at crossroads into Fulham Road.

CHESTER CITY FC

Founded: 1884	**Record Attendance**: 5,638 (2/4/94)
Turned Professional: 1902	**Colours**: Shirts - Blue and White Stripes
Limited Company: 1909	Shorts - Blue and White
Admitted to League: 1931	**Telephone No.**: (01244) 371376
Former Name(s): Chester FC	**Ticket Office**: (01244) 371376
Nickname: 'Blues' 'City'	**Pitch Size**: 115 × 75yds
Ground: The Deva Stadium, Bumpers Lane,	**Ground Capacity**: 6,000
Chester CH1 4LT	**Seating Capacity**: 3,500 (Approximately)

GENERAL INFORMATION

Supporters Club Administrator:
B. Hipkiss
Address: c/o Club
Telephone Number: (01244) 371376
Car Parking: Ample at Ground
Coach Parking: At Ground
Nearest Railway Station: Chester (1.5 miles)
Nearest Bus Station: Chester (0.75 mile)
Club Shop:
Opening Times: 9.00-5.00pm weekdays and Matchdays
Telephone No.: (01244) 390243
Postal Sales: Yes
Nearest Police Station: Chester (0.75 mile)
Police Force: Cheshire
Police Telephone No.: (01244) 350222

GROUND INFORMATION

Away Supporters' Entrances: South Terrace
Away Supporters' Sections: South Terrace (Covered)
Family Facilities: Location of Stand:
Jewson Family Area - East Stand
Capacity of Stand: 100 seats

ADMISSION INFO (1995/96 PRICES)

Adult Standing: £7.00
Adult Seating: £9.00   (concessions in
Child Standing: £4.50   Family Enclosure)
Child Seating: £6.00
Programme Price: £1.20
FAX Number: (01244) 390265

WEST STAND

SOUTH TERRACE (Away)

NORTH TERRACE

JEWSON FAMILY AREA
EAST STAND

Travelling Supporters Information:

Routes: From North: Take M56/A41 or A56 into Town Centre then follow Queensferry (A548) signs into Sealand Road. Turn left at Traffic Lights by 'Texas' into Bumpers Lane - ground is 0.5 mile at end of road; From East: Take A54 or A51 into Town Centre (then as North); From South: Take A41 or A483 into Town Centre (then as North); From West: Take A55/A494 or A548 and follow Queensferry signs towards Birkenhead A494 and after 1.25 miles bear left onto A548 (then as North).

CHESTERFIELD FC

Founded: 1866	**Record Attendance**: 30,968 (7/4/39)
Turned Professional: 1891	**Colours**: Shirts - Blue and White
Limited Company: 1921	Shorts - White
Admitted to League: 1899	**Telephone No.**: (01246) 209765
Former Name(s): Chesterfield Town FC	**Ticket Office**: (01246) 209765
Nickname: 'Spireites' 'Blues'	**Pitch Size**: 112 × 73yds
Ground: Recreation Ground, Saltergate,	**Ground Capacity**: 11,308
Chesterfield S40 4SX	**Seating Capacity**: 2,608

GENERAL INFORMATION
Supporters Club Administrator: -
Address: c/o Club
Telephone Number: -
Car Parking: Saltergate Car Parks (0.5 mile)
Coach Parking: By Police Direction
Nearest Railway Station: Chesterfield (1ml)
Nearest Bus Station: Chesterfield
Club Shop:
Opening Times: Matchdays only
Telephone No.: (01246) 231535
Postal Sales: Yes
Nearest Police Station: Chesterfield (0.75ml)
Police Force: Derbyshire
Police Telephone No.: (01246) 220100

GROUND INFORMATION
Away Supporters' Entrances: Cross Street Turnstiles
Away Supporters' Sections: Cross Street End (Open)
Family Facilities: Location of Stand:
Main Stand - Saltergate Corner
Capacity of Stand: 400
Away Families: None

ADMISSION INFO (1995/96 PRICES)
Adult Standing: £7.00
Adult Seating: £8.00 - £9.00
Child Standing: £3.50
Child Seating: £3.50 - £4.00
Programme Price: £1.20
FAX Number: (01246) 556799

COMPTON STREET SIDE

SALTERGATE SPION KOP

CROSS STREET END (Away)

MAIN STAND
ST. MARGARET'S DRIVE

Travelling Supporters Information:
Routes: From North: Exit M1 Junction 30 then take A619 into Town Centre. Follow signs Old Brampton into Saltergate; From South & East: Take A617 into Town Centre (then as North); From West: Take A619 1st exit at Roundabout, (when into Town) into Foljambe Road and follow to end, turn right into Saltergate.

COLCHESTER UNITED FC

Founded: 1937
Former Name(s): The Eagles
Nickname: 'U's'
Ground: Layer Road Ground, Colchester CO2 7JJ
Record Attendance: 19,072 (27/11/48)

Colours: Shirts - Royal Blue & White Stripes
Shorts - White
Telephone No.: (01206) 574042
Ticket Office: (01206) 574042
Pitch Size: 110 × 70yds
Ground Capacity: 7,944
Seating Capacity: 1,150

GENERAL INFORMATION
Supporters Club Administrator:
Pete Tucker
Address: c/o Club
Telephone Number: (01206) 574042
Car Parking: Street Parking
Coach Parking: Boadicea Way (0.25 mile)
Nearest Railway Station: Colchester North (2 miles)
Nearest Bus Station: Colchester Town Centre
Club Shop: At club, 2nd shop in Town Centre
Opening Times: At Club: Thursdays & Saturdays 9.30am-4.30pm
Town Centre: Monday-Saturday 9.00-5.30pm
Telephone No.: (01206) 574042 & 561180
Postal Sales: Yes
Nearest Police Station: Southway, Colchester (0.5 mile)
Police Force: Essex
Police Telephone No.: (01206) 762212

GROUND INFORMATION
Away Supporters' Entrances: Layer Road End Turnstiles
Away Supporters' Sections: Layer Rd. End (covered)
Family Facilities: **Location of Stand**:
Opposite Main Stand (Access from Layer Road)
Capacity of Stand: 1,508

ADMISSION INFO (1994/95 PRICES)
Adult Standing: £6.00 (Family Terrace £5.00)
Adult Seating: £6.50 - £8.00 (Family Terrace £8.00)
Child Standing: £4.00 (Family Terrace £2.00)
Child Seating: £4.50 - £5.50 (Family Terrace £4.00)
Programme Price: £1.20
FAX Number: (01206) 48700

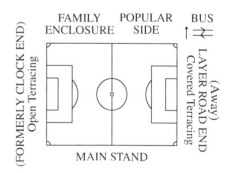

Travelling Supporters Information:
Routes: From North: Take A134/B1508 or A12 into Town Centre then follow signs to Layer (B1026) into Layer Road; From South: Take A12 and follow signs to Layer (B1026) into Layer Road; From West: Take A604 or A120 into Town Centre then follow Layer (B1026) signs into Layer Road.

COVENTRY CITY FC

Founded: 1883	**Record Attendance**: 51,455 (29/4/67)
Turned Professional: 1893	**Colours**: Shirts - Sky Blue/Navy & White Trim
Limited Company: 1907	Shorts - Sky Blue
Admitted to League: 1919	**Telephone No.**: (01203) 223535
Former Name(s): Singers FC (1883-1898)	**Ticket Office**: (01203) 225545
Nickname: 'Sky Blues'	**Pitch Size**: 110 × 76yds
Ground: Highfield Road Stadium,	**Ground Capacity**: 22,489 (All Seats)
King Richard Street, Coventry CV2 4FW	

GENERAL INFORMATION
Supporters Club Administrator: The Secretary
Address: Coventry City Supporters Club, Freehold Street, Coventry
Telephone Number: -
Car Parking: Street Parking
Coach Parking: By Police Direction
Nearest Railway Station: Coventry (1 mile)
Nearest Bus Station: Coventry (1 mile)
Bus Services to Ground: C16/C35/C36/C37/C7/C8/C24/C26/C27/C31A/C31C/C32/66/778
Club Shop: Thackhall St. & Cathedral Lanes
Opening Times: Daily except Sunday (Office hours)
Telephone No.: (01203) 257707
Postal Sales: Yes
Nearest Police Station: Little Park Street, Coventry (1 mile)
Police Force: West Midlands
Police Telephone No.: (01203) 539010

GROUND INFORMATION
Away Supporters' Entrances: Thackhall Street (Tickets from Away club)
Away Supporters' Sections: Mitchells & Butler Stand
Family Facilities: Location of Stand:
Co-op Bank Family Stand
Capacity of Stand: 2,500

ADMISSION INFO (1995/96 PRICES)
Adult Seating: £12.00 - £17.00
Child Seating: £6.00 - £8.50 (Members Only)
N.B. Prices vary depending on opponents
Programme Price: £1.50
FAX Number: (01203) 630318 (General Office)
               (01203) 258856 (Ticket Office)
Note: Children/OAPs pay adult prices unless members

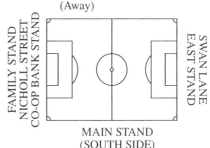

(THACKHALL STREET)
BUS MITCHELLS & BUTLERS STAND
(Away)

FAMILY STAND
NICHOLL STREET
CO-OP BANK STAND

SWAN LANE
EAST STAND

MAIN STAND
(SOUTH SIDE)
KING RICHARD STREET

Travelling Supporters Information:
Routes: From North, West & South: Exit M6 Junction 2. Take A4600 and follow signs for 'City Centre'. Follow this road for approximately 3 miles and, just under railway bridge turn right at traffic lights into Swan Lane. Stadium on left; From East: Take M45 then A45 to Ryton-on-Dunsmore. Take 3rd exit at roundabout (1.5 miles) A423, after 1.25 miles turn right (B4110), follow to T-junction, left then right into Swan Lane.

CREWE ALEXANDRA FC

Founded: 1877	**Record Attendance**: 20,000 (30/1/60)
Turned Professional: 1893	**Colours**: Shirts - Red
Limited Company: 1892	Shorts - White
Admitted to League: 1892	**Telephone No.**: (01270) 213014
Former Name(s): None	**Ticket Office**: (01270) 213014
Nickname: 'Railwaymen'	**Pitch Size**: 112 × 74yds
Ground: Gresty Road Ground, Crewe,	**Ground Capacity**: 5,900 Approximately
Cheshire CW2 6EB	**Seating Capacity**: 4,536

GENERAL INFORMATION

Supporters Club Administrator: Glynn Steele
Address: 18 Gresty Road, Crewe
Telephone Number: (01270) 255206
Car Parking: Car Park at Ground (200 cars)
Coach Parking: Car Park at Ground
Nearest Railway Station: Crewe (5 mins.)
Nearest Bus Station: Crewe Town
Club Shop: At Ground
Opening Times: Monday - Thursday
9.00am-5.00pm & Matchdays 9.00am-5.00pm
Telephone No.: (01270) 213014
Postal Sales: Yes
Nearest Police Station: Crewe Town (1 mile)
Police Force: Cheshire
Police Telephone No.: (01270) 500222

GROUND INFORMATION

Away Supporters' Entrances: Gresty Road Entrances
Away Supporters' Sections: Gresty Road End (Seated only)
Family Facilities: Location of Stand: Family Stand
Capacity of Stand: 650
Away Families: Yes

ADMISSION INFO (1995/96 PRICES)

Adult Standing: £8.00
Adult Seating: £9.50
Child Standing: £6.00
Child Seating: £7.00 (£3.00 in Family Stand - Junior Red Members Only)
Programme Price: £1.20
FAX Number: (01270) 216320
Note: Special concessions are available for members.

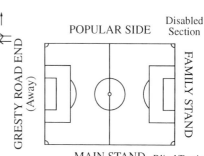

Travelling Supporters Information:

Routes: From North: Exit M6 Junction 17 take Crewe (A534) Road, and at Crewe roundabout follow Chester signs into Nantwich Road. Take left into Gresty Road; From South and East: Take A52 to A5020 to Crewe roundabout (then as North); From West: Take A534 into Crewe and turn right just before railway station into Gresty Road.

CRYSTAL PALACE FC

Founded: 1905	**Record Attendance**: 51,482 (11/5/79)
Turned Professional: 1905	**Colours**: Shirts - Red with Blue Stripes
Limited Company: 1905	Shorts - Red
Admitted to League: 1920	**Telephone No.**: (0181) 653-1000
Former Name(s): None	**Ticket Office**: (0181) 771-8841
Nickname: 'Eagles'	**Pitch Size**: 110 × 74yds
Ground: Selhurst Park, London, SE25 6PU	**Ground Capacity**: 26,500 (All Seats)

GENERAL INFORMATION
Supporters Club Administrator:
Terry Byfield
Address: c/o Club
Telephone Number: (0181) 653-1000
Car Parking: Street Parking/Sainsbury Car
Park near Ground
Coach Parking: Thornton Heath
Nearest Railway Station: Selhurst/Norwood
Junction (5 minutes walk)
Nearest Bus Station: Norwood Junction
Club Shop:
Opening Times: Weekdays & Matchdays
9.30-5.30
Telephone No.: (0181) 653-5584
Postal Sales: Yes
Nearest Police Station: South Norwood
(15 minutes walk)
Police Force: Metropolitan
Police Telephone No.: (0181) 653-8568

GROUND INFORMATION
Away Supporters' Entrances: Park Road
Away Supporters' Sections: Park Road Corner
Family Facilities: Location of Stand:
Members Stand (Clifton Road End)
Capacity of Stand: -

ADMISSION INFO (1994/95 PRICES)
Adult Seating: £16.00 to £20.00
Child Seating: £12.00 to £15.00
Programme Price: £1.30
FAX Number: (0181) 771-5311

Note: Prices vary depending on the game

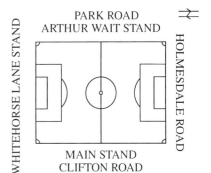

Travelling Supporters Information:
Routes: From North: Take M1/A1 to North Circular (A406) to Chiswick. Take South Circular (A205) to Wandsworth, take A3 to A214 and follow signs to Streatham to A23. Turn left onto B273 (1 mile), follow to end and turn left into High Street and into Whitehorse Lane; From East: Take A232 (Croydon Road) to Shirley and join A215 (Northwood Road), after 2.25 miles take left into Whitehorse Lane; From South: Take A23 and follow signs Crystal Palace B266 through Thornton Heath into Whitehorse Lane; From West: Take M4 to Chiswick (then as North).

DARLINGTON FC

Founded: 1883	**Record Attendance**: 21,023 (14/11/60)
Turned Professional: 1908	**Colours**: Shirts - White/Black
Limited Company: 1891	Shorts - Black
Admitted to League: 1921	**Telephone No.**: (01325) 465097
Former Name(s): None	**Ticket Office**: (01325) 465097
Nickname: 'Quakers'	**Pitch Size**: 110×74yds
Ground: Feethams Ground, Darlington	**Ground Capacity**: 5,006
DL1 5JB	**Seating Capacity**: 1,105

GENERAL INFORMATION
Supporters Club Administrator: K. Davies
Address: 60 Harrison Terrace, Darlington
Telephone Number: (01325) 350161
Car Parking: Street Parking
Coach Parking: By Police direction
Nearest Railway Station: Darlington
Nearest Bus Station: Darlington Central
Club Shop:
Opening Times: Monday-Friday 9.00-5.00
Telephone No.: (01325) 465097
Postal Sales: Yes
Nearest Police Station: Park Police Station,
Darlington (0.25 mile)
Police Force: Durham
Police Telephone No.: (01325) 467681

GROUND INFORMATION
Away Supporters' Entrances: Polam Lane Turnstiles
Away Supporters' Sections: West Terrace - Open
Family Facilities: **Location of Stand**:
West Stand
Capacity of Stand: 560
Away Families: Yes

ADMISSION INFO (1995/96 PRICES)
Adult Standing: £6.00
Adult Seating: £8.00   (£7.50 in Family Stand)
Child Standing: £3.00
Child Seating: £5.00   (£3.50 in Family Stand)
Programme Price: £1.20
FAX Number: (01325) 381377

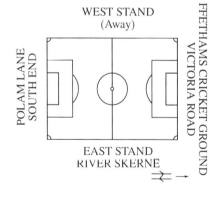

Travelling Supporters Information:
Routes: From North: Take A1(M) to A167 and follow road to Town Centre, then follow Northallerton signs to Victoria Road; From East: Take A67 to Town Centre (then as North); From South: Take A1(M) A66(M) into Town Centre and 3rd exit at second roundabout into Victoria Road; From West: Take A67 into Town Centre and 3rd exit at roundabout into Victoria Road.

DERBY COUNTY FC

Founded: 1884	**Record Attendance**: 41,826 (20/9/69)
Turned Professional: 1884	**Colours**: Shirts - White
Limited Company: 1896	Shorts - Black
Admitted to League: 1888 (Founder)	**Telephone No.**: (01332) 340105
Former Name(s): None	**Ticket Office**: (01332) 340105
Nickname: 'Rams'	**Pitch Size**: 110 × 71yds
Ground: Baseball Ground, Shaftesbury Crescent, Derby DE23 8NB	**Ground Capacity**: 17,665 (All Seats)

GENERAL INFORMATION
Supporters Club Administrator:
Mr. E. Hallam
Address: c/o Club
Telephone Number: (01332) 340105
Car Parking: Numerous Car Parks within 0.5 mile
Coach Parking: Russel St. Derby
Nearest Railway Station: Derby Midland (1 mile) and Ramsline Halt (specials only)
Nearest Bus Station: Derby Central
Club Shop:
Opening Times: Weekdays 9.30-5.00 & Matches
Telephone No.: (01332) 292081
Postal Sales: Yes
Nearest Police Station: Cotton Lane, Derby
Police Force: Derbyshire
Police Telephone No.: (01332) 290100

GROUND INFORMATION
Away Supporters' Entrances: Turnstiles 48-52
Away Supporters' Sections: Osmaston Stand, Lower & Middle Tiers
Family Facilities: Location of Stand: Vulcan Street End
Capacity of Stand: 3,500

ADMISSION INFO (1995/96 PRICES)
Adult Seating: £7.00 - £11.00
Child Seating: £4.00 - £6.00
Programme Price: £1.40
FAX Number: (01332) 293514

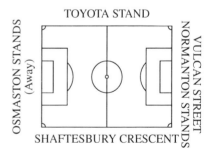

Travelling Supporters Information:
Routes: From North: Take A38 into City Centre then follow signs Melbourne (A514), turn right before Railway Bridge into Shaftesbury Street; From South, East & West: Take Derby Ring Road to Junction with A514 and follow signs to City Centre into Osmaston Road, after 1.25 miles take left turn into Shaftesbury Street.
Bus Services: Services 159, 188 and 189 pass near the Ground. Some Special services.

DONCASTER ROVERS FC

Founded: 1879
Turned Professional: 1885
Limited Company: 1920
Admitted to League: 1901
Former Name(s): None
Nickname: 'Rovers'
Ground: Belle Vue, Bawtry Road,
Doncaster   DN4 5HT

Record Attendance: 37,149 (2/10/48)
Colours: Shirts - Red
            Shorts - Red
Telephone No.: (01302) 539441
Ticket Office: (01302) 539441
Pitch Size: 110 × 76yds
Ground Capacity: 7,794
Seating Capacity: 1,259

GENERAL INFORMATION
Supporters Club Administrator: K. Avis
Address: 64 Harrowden Road, Wheatley,
Doncaster
Telephone Number: (01302) 365440
Car Parking: Large Car Park at Ground
Coach Parking: Car Park at Ground
Nearest Railway Station: Doncaster (1.5m)
Nearest Bus Station: Doncaster
Club Shop:
Opening Times: Monday & Thursday 10.00-
12.30. Matchdays: 1 hour before & after game
Telephone No.: (01302) 365440
Postal Sales: Yes
Nearest Police Station: College Road,
Doncaster
Police Force: South Yorkshire
Police Telephone No.: (01302) 366744

GROUND INFORMATION
Away Supporters' Entrances: Turnstiles A &
1, 2, 3, 4, 'A' Block
Away Supporters' Sections: Rossington Road
(Open) & Main Stand, 'A' Block
Family Facilities: Location of Stand:
Main Stand
Capacity of Stand: -

ADMISSION INFO (1995/96 PRICES)
Adult Standing: £7.00
Adult Seating: £9.00
Child Standing: £3.50
Child Seating: £5.00
Programme Price: £1.20
FAX Number: (01302) 539679

POPULAR SIDE STAND

ROSSINGTON END
(Away)

Enclosure
MAIN STAND
BAWTRY ROAD

BUS

Travelling Supporters Information:
Routes: From North: Take A1 to A638 into Town Centre, follow signs to Bawtry (A638), after 1.25 miles take 3rd exit from roundabout into Bawtry Road; From East: Take M18 to A630, after 2.75 miles take 1st exit at roundabout into A18, after 2.5 miles take 1st exit at roundabout into Bawtry Road; From South: Take M1 then M18, to A6182. After 2 miles 3rd exit at roundabout S/P 'Scunthorpe A18'. Then after 1.25 miles take 3rd exit at roundabout into Bawtry Road; From West: Take A635 into Town Centre and follow signs 'Bawtry' (then as South).

EVERTON FC

Founded: 1878	**Record Attendance**: 78,299 (18/9/48)
Turned Professional: 1885	**Colours**: Shirts - Blue
Limited Company: 1892	Shorts - White
Admitted to League: 1888 (Founder)	**Telephone No.**: (0151) 521-2020
Former Name(s): St.Domingo's FC (1878-79)	**Ticket Office**: (0151) 523-6666
Nickname: 'Blues' 'Toffeemen'	**Pitch Size**: 112 × 78yds
Ground: Goodison Park, Goodison Road.	**Ground Capacity**: 40,000 (All Seats)
Liverpool L4 4EL	

GENERAL INFORMATION
Supporters Club Administrator: The Secretary
Address: c/o Club
Telephone Number: (0151) 523-1614
Car Parking: Corner of Priory and Utting Av.
Coach Parking: Priory Road
Nearest Railway Station: Liverpool Lime Street
Nearest Bus Station: Brownlow Hill, Liverpool
Club Shop:
Opening Times: Weekdays & Matchdays 9.30-4.30 and Evening matches
Telephone No.: (0151) 521-2020 ext. 2253
Postal Sales: Yes - Mail Order & Credit Card
Nearest Police Station: Walton Lane, Liverpool
Police Force: Merseyside
Police Telephone No.: (0151) 709-6010

GROUND INFORMATION
Away Supporters' Entrances: Bullens Road
Away Supporters' Sections: Bullens Stand
Family Facilities: Location of Stand:
In front of Main Stand
Capacity of Stand: 2,080

ADMISSION INFO (1995/96 PRICES)
Adult Seating: £10.00 - £17.00
Child Seating: £6.00
Programme Price: £1.50
FAX Number: (0151) 523-9666
Note : Prices vary depending on the opponents

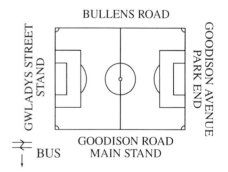

Travelling Supporters Information:
Routes: From North: Exit M6 junction 24. Take A58 Liverpool Road to A580 and follow into Walton Hall Avenue; From South & East: Exit M6 junction 21A to M62. At end of M62 turn right into Queen's Drive. After 3.75 miles turn left into Walton Hall Avenue; From North Wales: Cross Mersey into City Centre and follow signs to Preston (A580) into Walton Hall Avenue.
Bus Services: Service from City Centre - 19, 20, 21, F1, F9, F2, 30

40

EXETER CITY FC

Founded: 1904
Turned Professional: 1908
Limited Company: 1908
Admitted to League: 1920
Former Name(s): Formed by amalgamation of
St. Sidwell United FC & Exeter United FC
Nickname: 'Grecians'
Ground: St. James Park, Exeter   EX4 6PX

Record Attendance: 20,984 (4/3/31)
Colours: Shirts - Red & White Stripes
Shorts - White
Telephone No.: (01392) 54073
Ticket Office: (01392) 54073
Pitch Size: 114 × 73yds
Ground Capacity: 10,570
Seating Capacity: 1,690

GENERAL INFORMATION
Supporters Club Administrator: -
Address: c/o Club
Telephone Number: (01392) 54073
Car Parking: King William Street
Coach Parking: Paris Street Bus Station
Nearest Railway Station: Exeter St. James
Park (Adjacent)
Nearest Bus Station: Paris Street Bus Station
Club Shop:
Opening Times: Weekdays & Matchdays
9.00-5.00pm
Telephone No.: (01392) 54073
Postal Sales: Yes
Nearest Police Station: Heavitree Road,
Exeter (0.5 mile)
Police Force: Devon & Cornwall
Police Telephone No.: (01392) 52101

GROUND INFORMATION
Away Supporters' Entrances: St. James Road Turn-
stiles
Away Supporters' Sections: St.James Road Enclosure
Family Facilities: Location of Stand:
Block C - Grandstand
Capacity of Stand: -

ADMISSION INFO (1995/96 PRICES)
Adult Standing: £5.00 - £6.00
Adult Seating: £8.00
Child Standing: £3.00
Child Seating: £5.00
Programme Price: £1.50
FAX Number: (01392) 425885

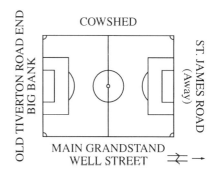

Travelling Supporters Information:
Routes: From North: Exit M5 junction 30 and follow signs to City Centre along Sidmouth Road and onto
Heavitree Road, take 4th exit at roundabout into Western Way and 2nd exit Tiverton Road, next left into St.
James Road; From East: Take A30 into Heavitree Road (then as North); From South & West: Take A38
and follow City Centre signs into Western Way and 3rd exit at roundabout into St. James Road.
Bus Services: Services A, D, J, K & S from City Centre,

FULHAM FC

Founded: 1879	**Record Attendance**: 49,335 (8/10/38)
Turned Professional: 1898	**Colours**: Shirts - White
Limited Company: 1903	Shorts - Black
Admitted to League: 1907	**Telephone No.**: (0171) 736-6561
Former Name(s): Fulham St. Andrew's FC	**Ticket Office**: (0171) 736-6561
(1879-1898)	**Pitch Size**: 110 × 75yds
Nickname: 'Cottagers'	**Ground Capacity**: 14,969
Ground: Craven Cottage, Stevenage Road,	**Seating Capacity**: 5,119
Fulham, London SW6 6HH	

GENERAL INFORMATION
Supporters Club Administrator:
Mr. M. Tenner
Address: c/o The Club
Telephone Number: (0171) 736-6561
Car Parking: Street Parking
Coach Parking: Stevenage Road
Nearest Railway Station: Putney
Nearest Tube Station: Putney Bridge (District)
Club Shop:
Opening Times: Home Matchdays, Monday, Wednesday & Friday afternoons 2.00-4.00pm
Telephone No.: (0171) 736-6561
Postal Sales: Yes
Nearest Police Station: Heckfield Place, Fulham
Police Force: Metropolitan
Police Telephone No.: (0171) 385-1212

GROUND INFORMATION
Away Supporters' Entrances: Putney End
Away Supporters' Sections: Putney Terrace (Open)
Family Facilities: Location of Stand:
Stevenage Road Stand ('B' Block)
Capacity of Stand: 377
Away Families: Accommodated in Family Stand

ADMISSION INFO (1995/96 PRICES)
Adult Standing: £7.50
Adult Seating: £11.00
Child Standing: £4.00
Child Seating: £5.50
Programme Price: £1.30
FAX Number: (0171) 731-7047

← ⇄ STEVENAGE ROAD STAND
(COTTAGE)

HAMMERSMITH END

PUTNEY END
(Away)

RIVERSIDE STAND
River Thames

Travelling Supporters Information:
Routes: From North: Take A1/M1 to North Circular (A406) West to Neasden and follow signs Harlesdon A404, then Hammersmith A219. At Broadway follow Fulham sign and turn right (1 mile) into Harbord Street left at end to Ground; From South & East: Take South Circular (A205) and follow Putney Bridge sign (A219), Cross Bridge and follow Hammersmith signs for 0.5 mile, left into Bishops Park Road, then right at end; From West: Take M4 to A4 then branch left (2 miles) into Hammersmith Broadway (then as North).
Bus Services: Services 74 & 220 from tube station to Ground.

GILLINGHAM FC

Founded: 1893	**Record Attendance**: 23,002 (10/1/48)
Turned Professional: 1894	**Colours**: Shirts - Blue
Limited Company: 1893	Shorts - White
Admitted to League: 1920	**Telephone No.**: (01634) 851854
Former Name(s): New Brompton FC	**Ticket Office**: (01634) 851462
1893-1913	**Pitch Size**: 114 × 75yds
Nickname: 'Gills'	**Ground Capacity**: 10,422
Ground: Priestfield Stadium, Redfern Avenue,	**Seating Capacity**: 1,225
Gillingham, Kent ME7 4DD	

GENERAL INFORMATION
Supporters Club Administrator:
Peter Lloyd
Address: c/o Club
Telephone Number: (01634) 851854
Car Parking: Street Parking
Coach Parking: By Police Direction
Nearest Railway Station: Gillingham
Nearest Bus Station: Gillingham
Club Shop:
Opening Times: Weekdays & Matchdays
10.00am-5.00pm
Telephone No.: (01634) 851462
Postal Sales: Yes
Nearest Police Station: Gillingham
Police Force: Kent
Police Telephone No.: (01634) 834488

GROUND INFORMATION
Away Supporters' Entrances: Redfern Avenue
Turnstiles
Away Supporters' Sections: Redfern Avenue Corner
(Gillingham End)
Family Facilities: Location of Stand:
Main Stand (Rainham End)
Capacity of Stand: 1,090

ADMISSION INFO (1995/96 PRICES)
Adult Standing: £7.00
Adult Seating: £9.00 - £11.50
Child Standing: £3.00 - £5.00
Child Seating: £7.00 - £10.00
Programme Price: £1.30
FAX Number: (01634) 850986

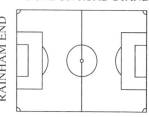

Travelling Supporters Information:
Routes: From All Parts: Exit M2 junction 4 and follow link road (dual carriageway) B278 to 3rd round-about. Turn left on to A2 (dual carriageway) across roundabout to traffic lights. Turn right Woodlands Road - after traffic lights. Ground 0.25 mile on left.

GRIMSBY TOWN FC

Founded: 1878
Turned Professional: 1890
Limited Company: 1890
Admitted to League: 1892
Former Name(s): Grimsby Pelham FC (1879)
Nickname: 'Mariners'
Ground: Blundell Park, Cleethorpes
DN35 7PY

Record Attendance: 31,651 (20/2/37)
Colours: Shirts - Black & White Stripes
Shorts - Black
Telephone No.: (01472) 697111
Ticket Office: (01472) 697111
Pitch Size: 111 × 74yds
Ground Capacity: 8,607 (All seats)

GENERAL INFORMATION
Supporters Club Administrator:
Rachel Branson
Address: 26 Humberstone Road, Grimsby
Telephone Number: (01472) 360050
Car Parking: Street Parking
Coach Parking: Harrington Street -
Near Ground
Nearest Railway Station: Cleethorpes (1.5
miles), New Clee (0.5 mile - specials only)
Nearest Bus Station: Brighowgate, Grimsby
(4 miles)
Club Shop: At ground (Shop Hours)
Opening Times: Monday-Friday 9.00-5.00
Match Saturdays 10.00-Kick-off
Telephone No.: (01472) 697111
Postal Sales: Yes
Nearest Police Station: Cleethorpes (Near
Railway Station) 1.5 miles
Police Force: Humberside
Police Telephone No.: (01472) 359171

GROUND INFORMATION
Away Supporters' Entrances: Harrington Street
Turnstiles 15-18, Constitutional Ave. Turnstiles 5-14
Away Supporters' Sections: Osmond Stand
Family Facilities: **Location of Stand**:
Main Stand (with access to family lounge)
Capacity of Stand: 120

ADMISSION INFO (1994/95 PRICES)
Adult Seating: £11.00 - £12.00 (Away fans £12.00)
Child Seating: £5.00 (No concessions for Away fans)
Programme Price: £1.30
FAX Number: (01472) 693665
N.B. Special Family Rate in Main Stand

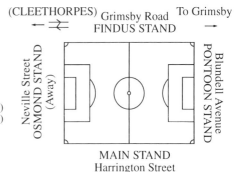

Travelling Supporters Information:
Routes: From All Parts except Lincolnshire and East Anglia: Take M180 to A180 follow signs to Grimsby/
Cleethorpes. A180 ends at roundabout (3rd in short distance after crossing Docks), take 2nd exit from roundabout over Railway flyover into Cleethorpes Road (A1098) and continue into Grimsby Road. After second
stretch of Dual Carriageway, Ground 0.5 mile on left; From Lincolnshire: Take A46 or A16 and follow
Cleethorpes signs along (A1098) Weelsby Road (2 miles) and take 1st exit at roundabout at end of Clee Road
into Grimsby Road. Ground 1.75 miles on right.

HARTLEPOOL UNITED FC

<table>
<tr><td>

Founded: 1908
Turned Professional: 1908
Limited Company: 1908
Admitted to League: 1921
Former Name(s): Hartlepools United FC
(1908-68); Hartlepool FC (1968-77)
Nickname: 'The Pool'
Ground: Victoria Ground, Clarence Road,
Hartlepool   TS24 8BZ

</td><td>

Record Attendance: 17,426 (15/1/57)
Colours: Shirts - Blue & Sky Blue
          Shorts - Blue & Sky Blue
Telephone No.: (01429) 272584
Ticket Office: (01429) 222077
Pitch Size: 113 × 77yds
Ground Capacity: 4,961
Seating Capacity: 2,800

</td></tr>
</table>

GENERAL INFORMATION

Supporters Club Administrator:
D. Lattimer
Address: 4 Friarage Gardens, Hartlepool
Telephone Number: -
Car Parking: Street Parking
Coach Parking: Church Street
Nearest Railway Station: Hartlepool Church
Street (5 minutes walk)
Nearest Bus Station: Church Street
Club Shop:
Opening Times: Weekdays 9.00am - 5.00pm
Saturdays 9.00am - 2.30pm
Telephone No.: (01429) 222077
Postal Sales: Yes
Nearest Police Station: Avenue Road,
Hartlepool
Police Force: Cleveland
Police Telephone No.: (01429) 221151

GROUND INFORMATION

Away Supporters' Entrances: Clarence Road
Turnstiles 1, 2 & 3
Away Supporters' Sections: Town End, Clarence Rd.
Family Facilities: **Location of Stand**:
Family Enclosure - Millhouse Stand
Capacity of Stand: -

ADMISSION INFO (1995/96 PRICES)

Adult Standing: £7.00
Adult Seating: £9.00
Child Standing: £5.00
Child Seating: £6.00
Programme Price: £1.20
FAX Number: (01429) 863007

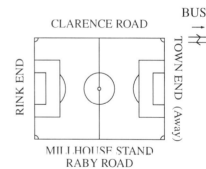

Travelling Supporters Information:

Routes: From North: Take A1/A19 then A179 towards Hartlepool to Hart. Straight across traffic lights (2.5 miles) to cross-roads, then turn left into Clarence Road; From South & West: Take A1/A19 or A689 into Town Centre then turn left into Middleton Road and left again into Clarence Road.

HEREFORD UNITED FC

Founded: 1924	**Record Attendance**: 18,114 (4/1/58)
Turned Professional: 1924	**Colours**: Shirts - White
Limited Company: 1939	Shorts - Black
Admitted to League: 1972	**Telephone No.**: (01432) 276666
Former Name(s): None	**Ticket Information**: (01432) 276666
Nickname: 'United' 'The Bulls'	**Pitch Size**: 111 × 74yds
Ground: Edgar Street, Hereford HR4 9JU	**Ground Capacity**: 13,752
	Seating Capacity: 2,897

GENERAL INFORMATION
Supporters Club Administrator:
K. Benjimen
Address: c/o Club
Telephone Number: (01432) 265005
Car Parking: Merton Meadow & Edgar Street Car Parks
Coach Parking: Cattle Market (Near Ground)
Nearest Railway Station: Hereford (0.5 mile)
Nearest Bus Station: Commercial Road, Hereford
Club Shop:
Opening Times: Matchdays & Weekdays via Commercial Office
Telephone No.: (01432) 276666
Postal Sales: Yes
Nearest Police Station: Bath Street, Hereford
Police Force: Hereford
Police Telephone No.: (01432) 276422

GROUND INFORMATION
Away Supporters' Entrances: Blackfriars Street and Edgar Street
Away Supporters' Sections: Blackfriars Street End
Family Facilities: **Location of Stand**:
Edgar Street Side
Capacity of Stand: 300

ADMISSION INFO (1995/96 PRICES)
Adult Standing: £6.00 - £7.00
Adult Seating: £8.00 - £9.00
Child Standing: £3.00 - £4.00
Child Seating: £5.00 - £6.00
Programme Price: £1.50
FAX Number: (01432) 341359
Note: Prices vary depending on League position.

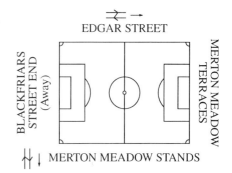

Travelling Supporters Information:
Routes: From North: Follow A49 Hereford signs straight into Edgar Street; From East: Take A465 or A438 into Hereford Town Centre, then follow signs for Leominster (A49) into Edgar Street; From South: Take A49 or A465 into Town Centre (then as East); From West: Take A438 into Town Centre (then as East).

HUDDERSFIELD TOWN FC

Founded: 1908	**Record Attendance**: 18,775 (6/5/95)
Turned Professional: 1908	**Colours**: Shirts - Blue & White Stripes
Limited Company: 1908	Shorts - Blue
Admitted to League: 1910	**Telephone No.**: (01484) 420335
Former Name(s): None	**Ticket Office**: (01484) 420335
Nickname: 'Terriers'	**Pitch Size**: 115×76yds
Ground: The Alfred McAlpine Stadium, Leeds Road, Huddersfield HD1 6PX	**Ground Capacity**: 20,000 (All Seats)

GENERAL INFORMATION

Supporters Club Administrator:
Mrs M. Procter
Address: 23 Lincroft Avenue, Dalton, Huddersfield, HD5 8DS
Telephone Number: (01484) 420335
Car Parking: Car Park for 1,100 cars adjacent
Coach Parking: Adjacent Car Park
Nearest Railway Station: Huddersfield (1.25 miles)
Nearest Bus Station: Huddersfield
Club Shop:
Opening Times: Weekdays 9.00am - 5.00pm & Saturday Matchdays 9.00am - 3.00pm
Telephone No.: (01484) 534867
Postal Sales: Yes
Nearest Police Station: Huddersfield (1 mile)
Police Force: West Yorkshire
Police Telephone No.: (01484) 422122

GROUND INFORMATION

Away Supporters' Entrances: Gardner Merchant Stand
Away Supporters' Sections: Gardner Merchant Stand
Family Facilities: **Location of Stand**:
Riverside Stand, Lower Tier
Capacity of Stand: 5,100

ADMISSION INFO (1995/96 PRICES)

Adult Seating: £9.00 to £13.00
Child Seating: £5.00 to £7.00
Programme Price: £1.50
FAX Number: (01484) 515122

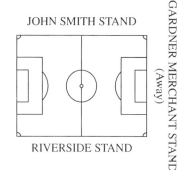

JOHN SMITH STAND

GARDNER MERCHANT STAND (Away)

RIVERSIDE STAND

Travelling Supporters Information:
Routes: From North, East & West: Exit M62 junction 25 and take the A644 and A62 following Huddersfield signs. Follow signs for Alfred McAlpine Stadium. From South: Leave M1 at Junction 38 then follow A637/A642 to Huddersfield. At Ring Road follow signs A62 Alfred McAlpine Stadium.
Bus Services: Services 220, 221, 201/2/3

HULL CITY FC

Founded: 1904
Turned Professional: 1904
Limited Company: 1904
Admitted to League: 1905
Former Name(s): None
Nickname: 'Tigers'
Ground: Boothferry Park, Boothferry Road, Hull   HU4 6EU

Record Attendance: 55,019 (26/2/49)
Colours: Shirts - Black & Amber
Shorts - Black
Telephone No.: (01482) 351119
Ticket Office: (01482) 351119
Pitch Size: 115 × 75yds
Ground Capacity: 14,996
Seating Capacity: 5,495

GENERAL INFORMATION

Supporters Club Administrator:
F. Anholm
Address: c/o Club
Telephone Number: (01482) 632987
Car Parking: Limited Parking at Ground
Street Parking and Schools
Coach Parking: At Ground
Nearest Railway Station: Hull Paragon
(1.5 miles)
Nearest Bus Station: Ferensway, Hull
(1.5 miles)
Club Shop: Paragon Square, Hull & at
Ground
Opening Times: Weekdays 9.30-4.30
Matchdays 10.00-3.00 - Ground
Telephone No.: (01482) 351119/328297
Postal Sales: Yes
Nearest Police Station: Central, Hull
(2 miles)
Police Force: Humberside
Police Telephone No.: (01482) 210031

GROUND INFORMATION

Away Supporters' Entrances: North Stand Turnstiles
Away Supporters' Sections: Visitor's enclosure,
North Stand plus seating area in West Stand
Family Facilities: Location of Stand:
Main Stand
Capacity of Stand: 568

ADMISSION INFO (1995/96 PRICES)

Adult Standing: £7.00
Adult Seating: £8.00 - £10.00
Child Standing: £3.00
Child Seating: £4.00 - £5.00
Programme Price: £1.30
FAX Number: (01482) 565752

Travelling Supporters Information:
Routes: From North: Take A1 or A19 then A1079 into City Centre and follow signs for Leeds (A63) into Anlaby Road. At roundabout (1 mile) take 1st exit into Boothferry Road; From West: Take M62 to A63 to Hull. Fork left after Ferriby Crest Motel to Humber Bridge roundabout, then take 1st exit to Boothferry Road (Ground 1.5 miles). Do NOT follow Clive Sullivan way; From South: Non-scenic alternative route take M18 to M62 (then as West). Or use motorways M1 to M18 then M180 and follow signs over Humber Bridge (Toll), take 2nd exit at roundabout (A63) towards Boothferry Road (Ground 1.5 miles).

IPSWICH TOWN FC

<table>
<tr><td>

Founded: 1887
Turned Professional: 1936
Limited Company: 1936
Admitted to League: 1938
Former Name(s): None
Nickname: 'Town' 'Super Blues'
Ground: Portman Road, Ipswich   IP1 2DA

</td><td>

Record Attendance: 38,010 (8/3/75)
Colours: Shirts - Blue with White Sleeves
Shorts - White
Telephone No.: (01473) 219211
Ticket Office: (01473) 221133
Pitch Size: 112 × 70yds
Ground Capacity: 22,559 (All Seats)

</td></tr>
</table>

GENERAL INFORMATION

Supporters Club Administrator:
Mr. G. Dodson
Address: c/o Club
Telephone Number: (01473) 219211
Car Parking: Portman Road and Portman Walk Car Parks
Coach Parking: Portman Walk
Nearest Railway Station: Ipswich (5 mins)
Nearest Bus Station: Ipswich
Club Shop:
Opening Times: Weekdays & Matchdays 9.00-5.00
Telephone No.: (01473) 214614
Postal Sales: Yes
Nearest Police Station: Civic Drive, Ipswich (5 minutes walk)
Police Force: Suffolk
Police Telephone No.: (01473) 55811

GROUND INFORMATION

Away Supporters' Entrances: Portman Road Turnstiles C & D
Away Supporters' Sections: Portman Road C & D
Family Facilities: **Location of Stand**:
South side of Pioneer Stand & Portman Lower Terrace
Capacity of Stands: Approximately 3,000

ADMISSION INFO (1995/96 PRICES)

Adult Seating: £9.00 - £16.00
Child Seating: £5.00 - £16.00
Programme Price: £1.50
FAX Number: (01473) 226835

PORTMAN ROAD (Away)
PORTMAN STAND

PORTMAN WALK
NORTH STAND

CHURCHMAN'S END
SOUTH STAND

PIONEER STAND
CONSTANTINE ROAD

Travelling Supporters Information:
Routes: From North & West: Take A14 following signs for Ipswich West only. Proceed through Constable Country Hotel traffic lights and at 2nd set of traffic lights turn right into West End Road, ground 0.25 mile along on left; From South: Follow signs for Ipswich West then as North and West.

LEEDS UNITED FC

Founded: 1919	**Record Attendance**: 57,892 (15/3/67)
Turned Professional: 1919	**Colours**: Shirts - White
Limited Company: 1919	Shorts - White
Admitted to League: 1920	**Telephone No.**: (0113) 271-6037
Former Name(s): Formed after Leeds City FC	**Ticket Office**: (0113) 271-0710
wound up for 'Irregular Practices'	**Pitch Size**: 117 × 76yds
Nickname: 'United'	**Ground Capacity**: 40,000 (All Seats)
Ground: Elland Road, Leeds LS11 0ES	

GENERAL INFORMATION
Supporters Club Administrator:
Eric Carlile
Address: c/o Club
Telephone Number: (0113) 271-6037
Car Parking: Large Car Parks (Adjacent)
Coach Parking: By Police Direction
Nearest Railway Station: Leeds City
Nearest Bus Station: Leeds City Centre -
Specials from Swinegate
Club Shop:
Opening Times: Weekdays 9.15-5.00,
Matchdays 9.15-Kick-off
Telephone No.: (0113) 270-6844
Postal Sales: Yes (send SAE)
Nearest Police Station: Holbeck, Leeds
(3 miles)
Police Force: West Yorkshire
Police Telephone No.: (0113) 243-5353

GROUND INFORMATION
Away Supporters' Entrances: South East Corner or
South Stand
Away Supporters' Sections: South East Corner or
South Stand
Family Facilities: Location of Stand:
East Stand
Capacity of Stand: 10,000

ADMISSION INFO (1995/96 PRICES)
Adult Seating: £14.00 - £25.00
Child Seating: Half-price for Members only
Programme Price: £1.50
FAX Number: (0113) 272-0370

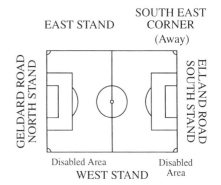

Travelling Supporters Information:
Routes: From North: Take A58 or A61 into City Centre and follow signs to M621; Leave Motorway after
1.5 miles and exit roundabout on to A643 into Elland Road; From North-East: Take A63 or A64 into City
Centre (then as North); From South: Take M1 to M621 (then as North); From West: Take M62 to M621
(then as North).

LEICESTER CITY FC

Founded: 1884	**Record Attendance**: 47,298 (18/2/28)
Turned Professional: 1894	**Colours**: Shirts - Blue with White Collars
Limited Company: 1894	Shorts - Blue
Admitted to League: 1894	**Telephone No.**: (0116) 255-5000
Former Name(s): Leicester Fosse FC	**Ticket Office**: (0116) 291-5232
(1884-1919)	**Pitch Size**: 112 × 75yds
Nickname: 'Filberts' 'Foxes'	**Ground Capacity**: 22,526 (All Seats)
Ground: City Stadium, Filbert Street,	
Leicester LE2 7FL	

GENERAL INFORMATION

Supporters Club Administrator:
C. Ginetta
Address: c/o Club
Telephone Number: (0116) 255-5000
Car Parking: NCP Car Park (5 mins. walk)
& Street Parking
Coach Parking: Sawday Street
Nearest Railway Station: Leicester (1 mile)
Nearest Bus Station: St.Margaret's (1 mile)
Club Shop:
Opening Times: Weekdays and Matchdays
9.00am - 5.30pm
Telephone No.: (0116) 255-9455
Postal Sales: Yes
Nearest Police Station: Charles Street,
Leicester
Police Force: Leicester
Police Telephone No.: (0116) 253-0066

GROUND INFORMATION

Away Supporters' Entrances: East Stand, Blocks T
& U
Away Supporters' Sections: Block T East Stand,
Block U North Stand
Family Facilities: **Location of Stand**:
Carling Family Enclosure
Capacity of Stand: 3,412

ADMISSION INFO (1995/96 PRICES)

Adult Seating: £10.00 - £17.00
Child Seating: £5.00 - £9.00
Programme Price: £1.50
FAX Number: (0116) 247-0585

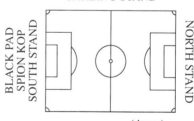

CARLING STAND

BLACK PAD
SPION KOP
SOUTH STAND

FAMILY CLUB
FILBERT STREET
NORTH STAND

BLOCK T.
(Away)

EAST STAND
BURNMOOR STREET

(Away)

Travelling Supporters Information:
Routes: From North: Take A46/A607 into City Centre or exit M1 junction 22 for City Centre, follow
'Rugby' signs into Almond Road, turn right at end into Aylestone Road, turn left into Walnut Street and left
again into Filbert Street; From East: Take A47 into City Centre (then as for North); From South: Exit M1
junction 21 and take A46, turn right 0.75 mile after Railway bridge into Upperton Road, then right into Filbert
Street; From West: Take M69 to City Centre (then as North).

LEYTON ORIENT FC

Founded: 1881
Turned Professional: 1903
Limited Company: 1906
Admitted to League: 1905
Former Name(s): Glyn Cricket & Football Club (1881/6); Eagle FC (1886/8); Clapton Orient FC (1888/1946); Leyton Orient FC (1946/66); Orient FC (1966/87)
Nickname: 'O's'

Record Attendance: 34,345 (25/1/64)
Colours: Shirts - Red
    Shorts - White
Telephone No.: (0181) 539-2223
Ticket Office: (0181) 539-2223
Pitch Size: 115 × 80yds
Ground Capacity: 17,065
Seating Capacity: 7,171

Ground: Leyton Stadium, Brisbane Road, Leyton, London   E10 5NE

GENERAL INFORMATION
Supporters Club Administrator: D.Dodd
Address: c/o Club
Telephone Number: (0181) 539-6156
Car Parking: NCP Brisbane Road & Street Parking
Coach Parking: By Police Direction
Nearest Railway Station: Leyton Midland Road (0.5 mile)
Nearest Tube Station: Leyton (Central)
Club Shop:
Opening Times: Monday-Friday (Wednesday closed) 10.00-4.30pm
Telephone No.: (0181) 539-2223
Postal Sales: Yes
Nearest Police Station: Francis Road, Leyton, London   E10
Police Force: Metropolitan
Police Telephone No.: (0181) 556-8855

GROUND INFORMATION
Away Supporters' Entrances: South Terrace Turnstiles
Away Supporters' Sections: South Terrace (Open)
Family Facilities: Location of Stand: North Wing
Capacity of Stand: not specified

ADMISSION INFO (1995/96 PRICES)
Adult Standing: £7.00
Adult Seating: £8.00, £9.00 or £11.00
Child Standing: £3.50
Child Seating: £4.00, £4.50 or £6.00
Programme Price: £1.20
FAX Number: (0181) 539-4390

OLIVER ROAD
WEST STAND

BUCKINGHAM ROAD
SOUTH TERRACE (Away)

WINDSOR ROAD
NORTH TERRACE

MAIN STAND
BRISBANE ROAD

Travelling Supporters Information:
Routes: From North & West: Take A406 North Circular and follow signs Chelmsford, to Edmonton, after 2.5 miles 3rd exit at roundabout towards Leyton (A112). Pass railway station and turn right (0.5 mile) into Windsor Road and left into Brisbane Road; From East: Follow A12 to London then City for Leytonstone follow Hackney signs into Grove Road, cross Main Road into Ruckholt Road and turn right into Leyton High Road, turn left (0.25 mile) into Buckingham Road, then left into Brisbane Road; From South: Take A102M through Blackwall Tunnel and follow signs to Newmarket (A102) to join A11 to Stratford, then signs Stratford Station into Leyton Road to railway station (then as North).

LINCOLN CITY FC

Founded: 1883	**Record Attendance**: 23,196 (15/11/67)
Turned Professional: 1892	**Colours**: Shirts - Red & White Stripes
Limited Company: 1892	Shorts - Black
Admitted to League: 1892	**Telephone No.**: (01522) 522224
Former Name(s): None	**Ticket Office**: (01522) 522224
Nickname: 'Red Imps'	**Pitch Size**: 110 × 76yds
Ground: Sincil Bank, Lincoln LN5 8LD	**Ground Capacity**: 10,918
	Seating Capacity: 9,246

GENERAL INFORMATION
Supporters Club Administrator: -
Address: c/o Club
Telephone Number: (0522) 522224
Car Parking: Adjacent to Ground (£2.00)
Coach Parking: South Common (300 yards)
Nearest Railway Station: Lincoln Central
Nearest Tube Station: Lincoln Central
Club Shop: At Ground, St. Andrews Stand
Opening Times: Weekdays & Matchdays
9.00-5.00
Telephone No.: (0522) 522224
Postal Sales: Yes
Nearest Police Station: West Parade, Lincoln
(1.5 miles)
Police Force: Lincolnshire
Police Telephone No.: (0522) 529911

GROUND INFORMATION
Away Supporters' Entrances: Linpave Stand
Away Supporters' Sections: Linpave Stand (Seating)
Family Facilities: Location of Stand:
St. Andrew's Stand & E.G.T. Family Stand
Capacity of Stand: 650

ADMISSION INFO (1995/96 PRICES)
Adult Standing: £5.00 - £5.50
Adult Seating: £5.50 - £7.50
Child Standing: £3.50
Child Seating: £4.50 - £5.50
Programme Price: £1.20
FAX Number: (01522) 520564

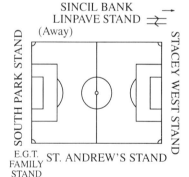

Travelling Supporters Information:
Routes: From East: Take A46 or A158 into City Centre following Newark (A46) signs into High Street and take next left (Scorer Street & Cross Street) for Ground; From North & West: Take A15 or A57 into City Centre then as East; From South: Take A1 to A46 for City Centre then into High Street and turn right into Scorer Street, then right again into Cross Street for Ground.

LIVERPOOL FC

Founded: 1892	**Colours**: Shirts - Red with White Markings
Turned Professional: 1892	Shorts - Red with White Markings
Limited Company: 1892	**Telephone No.**: (0151) 263-2361
Admitted to League: 1893	**Ticket Office**: (0151) 260-8680
Former Name(s): None	**Credit Card Bookings**: (0151) 263-5727
Nickname: 'Reds'	**Pitch Size**: 110×74yds
Ground: Anfield Road, Liverpool L4 0TH	**Ground Capacity**: 41,000 (All Seats)
Record Attendance: 61,905 (2/2/52)	

GENERAL INFORMATION
Supporters Club Administrator: -
Address: Liverpool International Supporters Club, c/o Club
Telephone Number: (0151) 263-2361
Car Parking: Stanley Park car park (adjacent)
Coach Parking: Priory Rd. & Pinehurst Ave.
Nearest Railway Station: Kirkdale
Nearest Bus Station: Paradise Street, Liverpool
Club Shop:
Opening Times: Monday-Saturday 9.30-5.30
Telephone No.: (0151) 263-1760
Postal Sales: Yes
Nearest Police Station: Walton Lane, Liverpool (1.5 miles)
Police Force: Merseyside
Police Telephone No.: (0151) 709-6010

GROUND INFORMATION
Away Supporters' Entrances: Anfield Road
Away Supporters' Sections: Visitors Section, Anfield Road (Covered)
Family Facilities: **Location of Stand**: Anfield Road End
Capacity of Stand: 3,000

ADMISSION INFO (1994/95 PRICES)
Adult Seating: Grade 'A' games £15   Grade 'B' £14
Child Seating: Grade 'A' games £6   Grade 'B' £5.00
Kop Seating: Grade 'A' games £11   Grade 'B' £10
Programme Price: £1.50
FAX Number: (0151) 260-8813
Ticket Office FAX: (0151) 261-1416
Note: Prices vary depending on opponents

CENTENARY STAND

ANFIELD ROAD (Away)

WALTON BRECK ROAD
SPION KOP STAND

PADDOCK ENCLOSURE
MAIN STAND
LOTHAIR ROAD

Travelling Supporters Information:
Routes: From North: Exit M6 junction 28 and follow Liverpool A58 signs into Walton Hall Avenue, pass Stanley Park and turn left into Anfield Road; From South & East: Take M62 to end of motorway then turn right into Queen's Drive (A5058) and turn left (3 miles) into Utting Avenue, after 1 mile turn right into Anfield Road; From North Wales: Take Mersey Tunnel into City Centre and follow signs to Preston (A580) into Walton Hall Avenue, turn right into Anfield Road before Stanley Park.

LUTON TOWN FC

Founded: 1885	**Record Attendance**: 30,069 (4/3/59)
Turned Professional: 1890	**Colours**: Shirts - White/Royal Blue/Orange
Limited Company: 1897	Shorts - Blue/Orange/White Trim
Admitted to League: 1897	**Telephone No.**: (01582) 411622
Former Name(s): Formed by amalgamation	**Ticket Office**: (01582) 30748
of Wanderers FC & Excelsior FC	**Pitch Size**: 110 × 72yds
Nickname: 'Hatters'	**Ground Capacity**: 10,499 (All Seats)
Ground: Kenilworth Road Stadium,	
1 Maple Road, Luton LU4 8AW	

GENERAL INFORMATION
Supporters Club Administrator:
Mrs.P.Gray
Address: 19 Kingsdown Avenue, Luton, Beds
Telephone Number: (01582) 391574
Car Parking: Street Parking
Coach Parking: Luton Bus Station
Nearest Railway Station: Luton (1 mile)
Nearest Bus Station: Bute Street, Luton
Club Shop: Kenilworth Road Forecourt
Opening Times: 9.00-5.00
Telephone No.: (01582) 411622
Postal Sales: Yes
Nearest Police Station:Buxton Road, Luton
(0.75 mile)
Police Force: Bedfordshire
Police Telephone No.: (01582) 401212

GROUND INFORMATION
Away Supporters' Entrances: Oak Road
Away Supporters' Sections: Oak Stand
Family Facilities: Location of Stand:
Kenilworth Stand
Capacity of Stand: 2,900

ADMISSION INFO (1995/96 PRICES)
Adult Seating: £8.00 - £15.50
Child Seating: £5.50 - £8.00
Programme Price: £1.50
FAX Number: (01582) 405070
Note : Lower prices apply when tickets are purchased
at least 14 days before the game and different prices
apply for certain cup games.

Travelling Supporters Information:
Routes: From North & West: Exit M1 junction 11 and follow signs to Luton (A505) into Dunstable Road.
Follow one-way system and turn right back towards Dunstable, take first left into Oak Road; From South &
East: Exit M1 junction 10 (or A6/A612) into Luton Town Centre and follow signs into Dunstable Road.
After railway bridge take sixth turning on left into Oak Road.

MANCHESTER CITY FC

Founded: 1887	**Record Attendance**: 84,569 (3/3/34)
Turned Professional: 1887	**Colours**: Shirts - Sky Blue
Limited Company: 1894	Shorts - White
Admitted to League: 1892	**Telephone No.**: (0161) 224-5000
Former Name(s): Ardwick FC (1887-94)	**Ticket Office**: (0161) 226-2224
Nickname: 'Citizens' 'City' 'Blues'	**Pitch Size**: 117 × 76yds
Ground: Maine Road, Moss Side,	**Ground Capacity**: 30,000 Approximately
Manchester M14 7WN	(All Seats)

GENERAL INFORMATION
Supporters Club Administrator: Frank Horrocks
Address: Manchester City Supporter's Club, Maine Road, Manchester M14 7WN
Telephone Number: (0161) 226-5047
Car Parking: Street Parking and Local Schools
Coach Parking: Kippax Street Car Park
Nearest Railway Station: Manchester Piccadilly (2.5 miles)
Nearest Bus Station: Chorlton Street
Club Shop:
Opening Times: Weekdays 9.30-5.00
Matchdays 9.30-5.30
Telephone No.: (0161) 226-4824
Postal Sales: Yes
Nearest Police Station: Platt Lane, Moss Side, Manchester
Police Force: Greater Manchester
Police Telephone No.: (0161) 872-5050

GROUND INFORMATION
Away Supporters' Entrances: North Stand
Away Supporters' Sections: North Stand
Family Facilities: Location of Stand: Umbro Stand
Capacity of Stand: Not specified

ADMISSION INFO (1994/95 PRICES)
Adult Seating: £12.00 to £15.00
Child Seating: £5.00 (Family Stand)
Programme Price: £1.50
FAX Number: (0161) 227-9418

KIPPAX STAND

(CLAREMONT ROAD)
NORTH STAND
(Away)

UMBRO STAND

MAIN STAND
(MAINE ROAD)

Travelling Supporters Information:
Routes: From North & West: Take M61 & M63 exit junction 9 following signs to Manchester (A5103). Turn right at crossroads (2.75 miles) into Claremont Road. After 0.25 mile turn right into Maine Road; From South: Exit M6 junction 19 to A556 and M56 junction 3 following signs to Manchester (A1503) (then as North); From East: Exit M62 onto the M602 Salford Motorway. Follow this to its end and then take the right hand lane and continue into Manchester along the A57. Pass Sainsburys and go under Railway Bridge heading for the Mancunian Way. After 2 roundabouts join Mancunian Way (elevated road) but leave at first exit and go under elevated section to roundabout then straight across. Follow road along past Dental Hospital into Lloyd Street and continue along to the ground.

MANCHESTER UNITED FC

Founded: 1878
Turned Professional: 1902
Limited Company: 1907
Admitted to League: 1892
Former Name(s): Newton Heath LYR FC
(1878-1892); Newton Heath FC (1892-1902)
Nickname: 'Red Devils'
Ground: Old Trafford, Manchester M16 0RA

Record Attendance: 76,962 (25/3/39)
Colours: Shirts - Red
Shorts - White
Telephone No.: (0161) 872-1661
Ticket Office: (0161) 872-0199
Pitch Size: 116 × 76yds
Ground Capacity: 55,300 (All Seats) To be
completed mid-1996

GENERAL INFORMATION
Supporters Club Administrator:
Barry Moorhouse
Address: c/o Club
Telephone Number: (0161) 872-5208
Car Parking: Lancashire Cricket Ground
(1,200 cars)
Coach Parking: By Police Direction
Nearest Railway Station: At Ground
Nearest Bus Station: Chorlton Street
Nearest Metro Station: Old Trafford
Club Shop:
Opening Times: Weekdays 9.30-5.00pm;
Matchdays 9.30-3.00pm; Sundays 10.00-
4.00pm; Non-Match Saturdays 9.30-4.00pm
Telephone No.: (0161) 872-3398
Postal Sales: Yes
Nearest Police Station: Talbot Road,
Stretford (0.5 mile)
Police Force: Greater Manchester
Police Telephone No.: (0161) 872-5050

GROUND INFORMATION
Away Supporters' Entrances: Stand L
Away Supporters' Sections: Stand L
Family Facilities: **Location of Stand**:
South Stand & Stretford End
Capacity of Stand: 4,100

ADMISSION INFO (1995/96 PRICES)
Adult Seating: Season ticket holders only
Child Seating: Season ticket holders only
Programme Price: £1.50
FAX Number: (0161) 896-5502
Note: Due to the redevelopment of the North Stand, it
is unlikely that matchday tickets will be available
during the 1995/96 season.

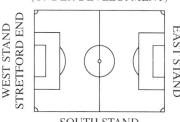

Travelling Supporters Information:
Routes: From North & West: Take M61 to M63 and exit junction 4 and follow Manchester signs (A5081).
Turn right (2.5 miles) into Warwick Road; From South: Exit M6 junction 19 take Stockport (A556) then
Altrincham (A56). From Altrincham follow Manchester signs. turn left into Warwick Road (6 miles); From
East: Exit M62 junction 17 then A56 to Manchester. Follow signs South then Chester (Chester Road), turn
right into Warwick Road (2 miles).

MANSFIELD TOWN FC

Founded: 1891
Turned Professional: 1910
Limited Company: 1910
Admitted to League: 1931
Former Name(s): Mansfield Wesleyans FC (1891-1905)
Nickname: 'Stags'
Ground: Field Mill Ground, Quarry Lane, Mansfield, Notts.

Record Attendance: 24,467 (10/1/53)
Colours: Shirts - Amber and Blue Stripes
Shorts - White
Telephone No.: (01623) 23567
Ticket Office: (01623) 23567
Pitch Size: 115 × 70yds
Ground Capacity: 7,073
Seating Capacity: 2,275

GENERAL INFORMATION
Supporters Club Administrator: Miss T.Brown
Address: 55 Rosecroft Drive, Edwards Lane Estate, Nottingham
Telephone Number: -
Car Parking: Large Car Park at Ground
Coach Parking: Adjacent
Nearest Railway Station: Mansfield Alfreton Parkway - 9 miles (no public transport)
Nearest Bus Station: Mansfield
Club Shop:
Opening Times: Weekdays & Matchdays 9.00-5.00
Telephone No.: (01623) 658070
Postal Sales: Yes
Nearest Police Station: Mansfield (0.25 mile)
Police Force: Nottinghamshire
Police Telephone No.: (01623) 22622

GROUND INFORMATION
Away Supporters'Entrances: Quarry Lane Turnstiles
Away Supporters' Sections: Quarry Lane End (Open)
Family Facilities: Location of Stand: Chad Family Stand
Capacity of Stand: 1,130
ADMISSION INFO (1995/96 PRICES)
Adult Standing: £8.00
Adult Seating: £10.00 (£8.00 in Family Stand)
Child Standing: £3.00
Child Seating: £5.00 (£4.00 in Family Stand)
Programme Price: £1.20
FAX Number: (01623) 25014

CHAD FAMILY STAND (Disabled)

NORTH STAND

QUARRY LANE (Away)

WEST STAND

Travelling Supporters Information:
Routes: From North: Exit M1 junction 29, take A617 to Mansfield. After 6.25 miles turn right at Leisure Centre into Rosemary Street. Carry on to Quarry Lane and turn right; From South & West: Exit M1 junction 28, take A38 to Mansfield, after 6.5 miles turn right at crossroads into Belvedere Street, turn right after 0.25 mile into Quarry Lane; From East: Take A617 to Rainworth, turn left at crossroads (3 miles) into Windsor Road and turn right at end into Nottingham Road, then left into Quarry Lane.

MIDDLESBROUGH FC

Founded: 1876
Turned Professional: 1889
Limited Company: 1892
Admitted to League: 1899
Former Name(s): None
Nickname: 'Boro'
Ground: Cellnet Riverside Stadium,
Middlesbrough, Cleveland   TS6 3RS

Record Attendance: 53,596 (27/12/49)
Colours: Shirts - Red with White Yoke
       Shorts - White
Telephone No.: (01642) 227227
Ticket Information: (01642) 227227
Pitch Size: 115 × 75yds
Ground Capacity: 29,832 (All Seats)

GENERAL INFORMATION
Supporters Club Secretary:
Simon Bolton
Address: c/o Club
Telephone Number: (01642) 470512
Car Parking: 1,250 spaces (Season Ticket
holders only)
Coach Parking: At Ground
Nearest Railway Station: Middlesbrough
(0.25 mile)
Nearest Bus Station: Middlesbrough
Club Shop:
Opening Times: Monday-Friday 9.30-5.00
+ Saturdays 10.00-12.00 + Matchdays
Telephone No.: (01642) 227227
Postal Sales: Yes
Nearest Police Station: Dunning Street,
Middlesbrough (1 mile)
Police Force: Cleveland
Police Telephone No.: (01642) 248184

GROUND INFORMATION
Away Supporters' Entrances: South Stand Turnstiles
Away Supporters' Sections: South Stand
Family Facilities: Location of Stand:
West & East Stand Terraces & South Stand
Capacity of Stand: Not Specified

ADMISSION INFO (1995/96 PRICES)
Adult Seating: £10.00 - £15.00   (£8.00 in Family
Child Seating: £4.00 - £15.00   Group)
Programme Price: £1.50
FAX Number: Not allocated at time of publication

WEST STAND

SOUTH STAND

NORTH STAND

EAST STAND

Travelling Supporters Information:
Routes: From North: Take A19 across flyover and join A66 (Eastbound). At the end of the flyover, turn left at North Ormesby roundabout. The Ground is 200 metres down the road; From South: Take A1 & A19 to junction with A66 (Eastbound). After the flyover, turn left at the North Ormesby roundabout.

MILLWALL FC

Founded: 1885
Turned Professional: 1893
Limited Company: 1894
Admitted to League: 1920
Former Name(s): Millwall Rovers FC (1885-1893)   Millwall Athletic FC (1893-1925)
Nickname: 'Lions'
Ground: The New Den, London   SE16

Record Attendance: 20,093 (10/1/94
vs Arsenal)
Colours: Shirts - Blue
Shorts - White
Telephone No.: (0171) 232-1222
Ticket Office: (0171) 231-9999
Pitch Size: 112 × 74yds
Ground Capacity: 20,146 (All Seats)

GENERAL INFORMATION
Supporters Club Administrator: None
Address: -
Telephone Number: -
Car Parking: Juno Way
Coach Parking: Adjacent to Ground
Nearest Railway Station: New Cross Gate/ South Bermondsey (0.5 mile)
Nearest Tube Station: New Cross Gate/ Surrey Quays (0.5 mile)
Club Shop: Next to Stadium
Opening Times: Daily 9.30-4.30
Telephone No.: (0171) 231-9845
Postal Sales: Yes
Nearest Police Station: Deptford/Lewisham (1 mile)
Police Force: Metropolitan
Police Telephone No.: (0171) 679-9217

GROUND INFORMATION
Away Supporters' Entrances: North East Stand Turnstiles **31-36**
Away Supporters' Sections: North Stand
Family Facilities: Location of Stand: Upper Tier East Stand
Capacity of Stand: 800

ADMISSION INFO (1995/96 PRICES)
Adult Seating: £10.00 - £20.00
Child Seating: £5.00
Senior Citizens: £4.50 - £10.00
Programme Price: £1.50
FAX Number: (0171) 231-3663

WEST STAND

SOUTH STAND

NORTH STAND (Away)

EAST STAND

Travelling Supporters Information:
Routes: From North: Follow City signs from M1/A1 then signs for Shoreditch and Whitechapel. Follow signs Ring Road, Dover, cross over Tower Bridge, take 1st exit at roundabout (1 mile) onto A2. From Elephant & Castle take A2 (New Kent Road) into Old Kent Road and turn left (after 4 miles) at Canterbury Arms Pub into Ilderton Road then follow Surrey Canal Road to new ground in Zampa Road; From South: Take A20 and A21 following signs to London. At New Cross follow signs for stadium; From East: Take A2 to New Cross (then as South); From West: From M4 and M3 follow South Circular (A205) following signs for Clapham, City A3 then Camberwell, New Cross and then then as South.

NEWCASTLE UNITED FC

Founded: 1882
Turned Professional: 1889
Limited Company: 1890
Admitted to League: 1893
Former Name(s): Newcastle East End FC
(1882-92) Became 'United' when amalgamated
with Newcastle West End FC
Nickname: 'Magpies'

Record Attendance: 68,386 (3/9/30)
Colours: Shirts - Black and White Stripes
        Shorts - Black
Telephone No.: (0191) 232-8361
Ticket Office: (0191) 261-1571
Pitch Size: 110 × 73yds
Ground Capacity: 36,649 (All Seats)

Ground: St.James Park, Newcastle-Upon-Tyne   NE1 4ST

GENERAL INFORMATION

Supporters Club Administrator: -
Address: -
Telephone Number: -
Car Parking: Street Parking
Coach Parking: By Police Direction
Nearest Railway Station: Newcastle Central (0.5 mile)
Nearest Bus Station: Gallowgate (0.25 mile)
Club Shop: At Ground, Eldon Square, Haymarket and MetroCentre
Opening Times: All shops are open Monday to Saturday 9.00-5.00. Eldon open until 8.00pm on Thursdays. MetroCentre open until at least 7.00pm Monday-Saturday.
Telephone No.: (0191) 261-6357
Postal Sales: Yes
Phone: (0191) 232-4080
Nearest Police Station: Market Street, Newcastle
Police Force: Northumbria
Police Telephone No.: (0191) 232-3451

GROUND INFORMATION

Away Supporters' Entrances: North East Corner
Away Supporters' Sections: Sir John Hall Stand
Family Facilities: Location of Stand:
East Stand Paddock
Capacity of Stand: 792 seated

ADMISSION INFO (1994/95 PRICES)

Adult Seating: £15.00
Child Seating: £12.50
Programme Price: £1.50
FAX Number: (0191) 232-9875
Note: It is expected that only Season Ticket Holders
will be admitted in 1995/96.

```
            ST. JAMES STREET
             EAST STAND
  ┌─────────────────────────────┐
  │                             │  STRAWBERRY PLACE
SIR JOHN HALL STAND    EXHIBITION STAND
  │                             │
  └─────────────────────────────┘
       MILBURN STAND
     BARRACK ROAD  ⇄ BUS →
```

Travelling Supporters Information:

Routes: From North: Follow A1 into Newcastle, then Hexham signs into Percy Street. Turn right into Leazes Park Road; From South: Take A1M, then after Birtley Granada Services take A69 Gateshead Western Bypass (bear left on Motorway). Follow Airport signs for approximately 3 miles then take A692 (Newcastle) sign, crossing the Redheugh Bridge. At roundabout take 3rd exit (Blenheim Street). Proceed over two sets of traffic lights crossing Westmorland Road and Westgate Road. Turn left into Bath Lane. Over traffic lights to next roundabout and take third exit into Barrack Road; From West: Take A69 towards City Centre. Pass Newcastle General Hospital. At traffic lights immediately after Hospital turn left into Brighton Grove and after 70 yards turn right into Stanhope Street. Proceed into Barrack Road.

NORTHAMPTON TOWN FC

Founded: 1897	**Record Attendance**: 7,461 vs Barnet 15/10/94
Turned Professional: 1901	**Colours**: Shirts - Claret
Limited Company: 1901	Shorts - White
Admitted to League: 1920	**Telephone No.**: (01604) 757773
Former Name(s): None	**Ticket Office**: (01604) 757773
Nickname: 'Cobblers'	**Pitch Size**: 112 × 75yds
Ground: Sixfields Stadium, Upton Way,	**Ground Capacity**: 7,653 (All Seats)
Northampton	

GENERAL INFORMATION
Supporters Club Administrator:
Alec Smith
Address: c/o Club
Telephone Number: (01604) 842636
Car Parking: At Ground
Coach Parking: At Ground
Nearest Railway Station: Northampton
Castle (2 miles)
Nearest Bus Station: Greyfriars
Club Shop:
Opening Times: Weekdays - 9.00-5.00pm
Matchdays 9.00-6.00
Telephone No.: (01604) 757773
Postal Sales: Yes
Nearest Police Station: Cambell Square,
Northampton
Police Force: Northants
Police Telephone No.: (01604) 33221

GROUND INFORMATION
Away Supporters' Entrances: South Stand
Away Supporters' Sections: South & East Stands
Family Facilities: **Location of Stand**:
East Stand and West Stand
Capacity of Stand: -

ADMISSION INFO (1995/96 PRICES)
Adult Seating: £7.50 to £12.00
Child Seating: £4.00 to £7.00
Programme Price: £1.20
FAX Number: (01604) 751613

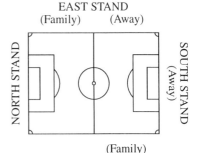

EAST STAND
(Family)   (Away)

NORTH STAND

SOUTH STAND
(Away)

(Family)
WEST STAND

Travelling Supporters Information:
Routes: From All Parts: Exit the M1 at junction 15A following the signs for Sixfields Leisure Centre onto Upton Way - the Ground is approximately 2 miles.

NORWICH CITY FC

Founded: 1902	**Record Attendance**: 43,984 (30/3/63)
Turned Professional: 1905	**Colours**: Shirts - Yellow
Limited Company: 1905	Shorts - Green
Admitted to League: 1920	**Telephone No.**: (01603) 760760
Former Name(s): None	**Ticket Office**: (01603) 761661
Nickname: 'Canaries'	**Pitch Size**: 114 × 74yds
Ground: Carrow Road, Norwich NR1 1JE	**Ground Capacity**: 21,994 (All Seats)

GENERAL INFORMATION
Supporters Club Administrator:
Kevan Platt
Address: Club Canary, Carrow Road, Norwich
Telephone Number: (01603) 760760
Car Parking: City Centre Car Parks (nearby)
Coach Parking: Lower Clarence Road
Nearest Railway Station: Norwich Thorpe (1 mile)
Nearest Bus Station: Surrey Street, Norwich
Club Shop: (In City Stand)
Opening Times: Weekdays & Matchdays 9.00am   -4.45pm
Telephone No.: (01603) 761125
Postal Sales: Yes
Nearest Police Station: Bethel Street, Norwich (1 mile)
Police Force: Norfolk
Police Telephone No.: (01603) 768769

GROUND INFORMATION
Away Supporters' Entrances: Turnstiles 1-3 - Barclay End
Away Supporters' Sections: South Stand - Blocks F, G & H (Covered)
Family Facilities: Location of Stand: South Stand
Capacity of Stand: 1,630

ADMISSION INFO (1995/96 PRICES)
Adult Seating: £10.00 - £15.00
Child Seating: £5.00 - £10.00
Programme Price: £1.50
FAX Number: (01603) 665510
Note: Prices vary according to the category of game.

SOUTH STAND (Disabled)
(Away)

CARROW ROAD
BARCLAY STAND

RIVER END STAND

CITY STAND
CARROW ROAD

Travelling Supporters Information:
Routes: From South: Take A11 or A140 and turn right onto A47 towards Great Yarmouth & Lowestoft, take A146 Norwich/Lowestoft sliproad, turn left towards Norwich and follow road signs for the Football Ground; From West: Take A47 on to A146 Norwich/Lowestoft slip road. Turn left towards Norwich, follow the road signs for the Football Ground.

NOTTINGHAM FOREST FC

Founded: 1865	**Record Attendance**: 49,945 (28/10/67)
Turned Professional: 1889	**Colours**: Shirts - Red
Limited Company: 1982	Shorts - White
Admitted to League: 1892	**Telephone No.**: (0115) 952-6000
Former Name(s): None	**Ticket Office**: (0115) 592-6002
Nickname: 'Reds' 'Forest'	**Pitch Size**: 115 × 78yds
Ground: City Ground, Nottingham	**Ground Capacity**: 30,564 (All Seats)
NG2 5FJ	

GENERAL INFORMATION

Supporters Club Administrator:
Mr. B. Tewson
Address: c/o Club
Telephone Number: (0115) 952-6000
Car Parking: East Car Park (300 cars) &
Street Parking
Coach Parking: East Car Park, Meadow Lane
Nearest Railway Station: Nottingham
Midland (0.5 mile)
Nearest Bus Station: Victoria Street/
Broadmarsh Centre
Club Shop:
Opening Times: Weekdays 9.00am - 5.00pm
Matchdays 9.00am - 3.00pm
Telephone No.: (0115) 952-6026
Postal Sales: Yes
Nearest Police Station: Rectory Road, West
Bridgford (1 mile)
Police Force: Nottinghamshire
Police Telephone No.: (0115) 948-1888

GROUND INFORMATION

Away Supporters' Entrances: Via East Car Park
Away Supporters' Sections: Bridgford Stand Lower
Tier
Family Facilities: **Location of Stand**:
Blocks G & Q Trent End
Capacity of Stand: -

ADMISSION INFO (1995/96 PRICES)

Adult Seating: £16.00 - £18.00
Child Seating: £8.00 (Family Section Only)
Programme Price: £1.50
FAX Number: (0115) 952-6003

EXECUTIVE STAND

TRENT END

BRIDGFORD STAND (Away)

MAIN STAND
PAVILION ROAD

Travelling Supporters Information:

Routes: From North: Exit M1 junction 26 following Nottingham signs (A610) then Melton Mowbray and Trent Bridge (A606) signs. Cross River Trent, left into Radcliffe Road then left into Colwick Road; From South: Exit M1 junction 24 following signs Nottingham (South) to Trent Bridge. Turn right into Radcliffe Road then left into Colwick Road; From East: Take A52 to West Bridgford, turn right into Colwick Road; From West: Take A52 into Nottingham following signs Melton Mowbray and Trent Bridge, cross River Trent (then as North).

Notts County FC

Founded: 1862 (Oldest in League)	**Record Attendance**: 47,310 (12/3/55)
Turned Professional: 1885	**Colours**: Shirts - Black and White Stripes
Limited Company: 1888	Amber Sleeve & Trim
Admitted to League: 1888 (Founder)	Shorts - White
Former Name(s): None	**Telephone No.**: (0115) 952-9000
Nickname: 'Magpies'	**Ticket Office**: (0115) 955-7210
Ground: Meadow Lane, Nottingham	**Pitch Size**: 117 × 76yds
NG2 3HJ	**Ground Capacity**: 20,300 (All Seats)

GENERAL INFORMATION

Supporters Club Administrator: P. Dennis
Address: c/o Club
Telephone Number: (0115) 955-7255
Car Parking: British Waterways, Meadow Lane
Coach Parking: Incinerator Road (Cattle Market Corner)
Nearest Railway Station: Nottingham Midland (0.5 mile)
Nearest Bus Station: Broadmarsh Centre
Club Shop:
Opening Times: Weekdays & Matchdays 9.00-5.30pm. Other Saturdays 9.00-12.00
Telephone No.: (0115) 952-9000
Postal Sales: Yes
Nearest Police Station: Station Street, Nottingham
Police Force: Nottinghamshire
Police Telephone No.: (0115) 948-1888

GROUND INFORMATION

Away Supporters' Entrances: Cattle Market Corner, Iremonger Road
Away Supporters' Sections: The Kop Stand
Family Facilities: **Location of Stand**: Family Stand - Meadow Lane End
Capacity of Stand: 2,139

ADMISSION INFO (1995/96 PRICES)

Adult Seating: £10.00 - £14.00
Child Seating: £5.00 - £7.00
Programme Price: £1.30
FAX Number: (0115) 955-3994

JIMMY SIRRELL STAND
Disabled

(CATTLE MARKET ROAD)
THE KOP STAND (Away)

DEREK PAVIS STAND

(SPORTS CENTRE)
MEADOW LANE
FAMILY STAND

Travelling Supporters Information:
Routes: From North: Exit M1 junction 26 following Nottingham signs (A610) then Melton Mowbray and Trent Bridge (A606) signs. Before River Trent turn left into Meadow Lane; From South: Exit M1 junction 24 following signs Nottingham (South) to Trent Bridge, cross River and follow one-way system to the right, then turn left and right at traffic lights then second right into Meadow Lane; From East: Take A52 to West Bridgford/Trent Bridge, cross River and follow one-way system to the right then turn left and right at traffic lights, then second right into Meadow Lane; From West: Take A52 into Nottingham following signs Melton Mowbray and Trent Bridge, before River Trent turn left into Meadow Lane.

OLDHAM ATHLETIC FC

Founded: 1895	**Record Attendance**: 47,671 (25/1/30)
Turned Professional: 1899	**Colours**: Shirts - Blue
Limited Company: 1906	Shorts - Blue
Admitted to League: 1907	**Telephone No.**: (0161) 624-4972 (24 hours)
Former Name(s): Pine Villa FC (1895-99)	**Ticket Office**: (0161) 624-4972
Nickname: 'Latics'	**Pitch Size**: 110 × 74yds
Ground: Boundary Park, Oldham OL1 2PA	**Ground Capacity**: 13,700 (All Seats)

GENERAL INFORMATION
Supporters Club Administrator:
John Stanley
Address: c/o Club
Telephone Number: (0161) 624-4972
Car Parking: Lookers Stand Car Park
(1,000 cars)
Coach Parking: At Ground
Nearest Railway Station: Oldham Werneth
(1.5 miles)
Nearest Bus Station: Oldham Mumps
(2 miles)
Club Shop:
Opening Times: Mondays-Saturdays
9.00-5.00
Telephone No.: (0161) 652-0966
Postal Sales: Yes
Nearest Police Station: Chadderton
Police Force: Greater Manchester
Police Telephone No.: (0161) 624-0444

GROUND INFORMATION
Away Supporters' Entrances: Rochdale Road
Turnstiles
Away Supporters' Sections: Rochdale Road Stand
(seating)
Family Facilities: **Location of Stand**:
Lookers Stand
Capacity of Stand: 1,433

ADMISSION INFO (1995/96 PRICES)
Adult Seating: £7.50 - £13.00   (Away Fans £12.00)
Child Seating: £6.50 - £8.00   (Away Fans £8.00)
Programme Price: £1.50
FAX Number: (0161) 627-5915

Travelling Supporters Information:
Routes: From All Parts: Exit M62 junction 20 and take A627M to junction with A664. Take 1st exit at roundabout on to Broadway, then 1st right into Hilbre Avenue which leads to car park.

OXFORD UNITED FC

Founded: 1893
Turned Professional: 1949
Limited Company: 1949
Admitted to League: 1962
Former Name(s): Headington United FC (1893-1960)
Nickname: 'U's'
Ground: Manor Ground, London Road, Headington, Oxford OX3 7RS

Record Attendance: 22,730 (29/2/64)
Colours: Shirts - Yellow with Navy Sleeves
Shorts - Navy with Yellow Trim
Telephone No.: (01865) 61503
Ticket Office: (01865) 61503
Pitch Size: 110 × 75yds
Ground Capacity: 9,572
Seating Capacity: 2,777

GENERAL INFORMATION
Supporters Club Administrator: Gary Whiting
Address: c/o Club
Telephone Number: (01865) 63063
Car Parking: Street Parking
Coach Parking: Off Headley Way in Franklin Road
Nearest Railway Station: Oxford (3 miles)
Nearest Bus Station: Queen's Lane (2 miles)
Club Shop: Score Sports, Headington
Opening Times: Monday-Saturday 9.30am - 5.30pm (closes 3.00pm Matchdays)
Telephone No.: (01865) 65128
Postal Sales: Members only
Nearest Police Station: Cowley (2 miles)
Police Force: Thames Valley
Police Telephone No.: (01865) 749909

GROUND INFORMATION
Away Supporters' Entrances: Cuckoo Lane Turnstiles 5-11
Away Supporters' Sections: Cuckoo Lane Stand
Family Facilities: Location of Stand:
Beech Road Side (Members only)
Capacity of Stand: 162 uncovered seating,
306 covered seating

ADMISSION INFO (1995/96 PRICES)
Adult Standing: £8.00 - £8.50 (Prices vary
Adult Seating: £11.00   according to
Child Standing: £5.00 - £5.50   the category
Child Seating: £7.50   of match)
Programme Price: £1.30
FAX Number: (01865) 741820

OSLER ROAD

CUCKOO LANE (Away) · LONDON ROAD

Disabled Section · BEECH ROAD

Travelling Supporters Information:
Routes: From North: Exit M40 at Junction 9. Follow signs for A34 to Oxford. Take slip road A44 marked Witney, Woodstock. At roundabout take first exit (Pear Tree). Follow to next roundabout A44 junction with A40 Woodstock Road, take second exit marked A40 London. Down to next roundabout (Banbury Road), take second exit on to Northern by-pass. Cars should take next left turn at slip road marked New Marston 0.5 mile and JR Hospital 1 mile. (Coaches should follow diversions to avoid weak bridge, next roundabout A40 (Green Road), take fifth exit, follow signs for A40 junction with B4105 Marston.) Down to mini roundabout turn left. Straight up Headley Way, coaches should take second junction right marked Franklin Road which leads into Coach park. Cars - side street parking only. Take care for matchday parking restrictions. From South: A34 by-pass to junction A44 Pear Tree. Then as North. From East: Cars & Coaches should follow diversion directions as from Green Road Roundabout. From West: Take A34 following signs to M40. Take exit A44 marked Woodstock, take third exit Pear Tree, then as North.
Bus Services: Service 1 Railway Station to Queen's Lane, Service 2 to Ground.

PETERBOROUGH UNITED FC

Founded: 1923
Turned Professional: 1934
Limited Company: 1934
Admitted to League: 1960
Former Name(s): Peterborough & Fletton United FC (1923-34)
Nickname: 'Posh'
Ground: London Road, Peterborough, Cambs   PE2 8AL

Record Attendance: 30,096 (20/2/65)
Colours: Shirts - Blue
Shorts - White
Telephone No.: (01733) 63947
Ticket Information: (01733) 63947
Pitch Size: 112 × 72yds
Ground Capacity: 14,300
Seating Capacity: 4,715 (Will alter when Glebe Road Stand is completed)

GENERAL INFORMATION
Supporters Club Administrator: Ray Duke
Address: c/o Club
Telephone Number: -
Car Parking: Ample Parking at Ground
Coach Parking: Rear of Ground
Nearest Railway Station: Peterborough (1 mile)
Nearest Bus Station: Peterborough (0.25 mile)
Club Shop:
Opening Times: Monday to Friday 9.00am - 5.00pm
Telephone No.: (01733) 69760
Postal Sales: Yes
Nearest Police Station: Bridge Street, Peterborough (5 minutes walk)
Police Force: Cambridgeshire
Police Telephone No.: (01733) 63232

GROUND INFORMATION
Away Supporters' Entrances: Turnstile A, Moys End
Away Supporters' Sections: Moys End (Covered Standing) - Block A seating
Family Facilities: Location of Stand: Family Stand
Capacity of Stand: 3,500

ADMISSION INFO (1995/96 PRICES)
Adult Standing: £7.00
Adult Seating: £11.00 (Wings End £9.00)
Child Standing: £3.50 (Home fans only)
Child Seating: £5.50   (Wings End £4.50)
Programme Price: £1.00
FAX Number: (01733) 557210

GLEBE ROAD STAND

MOYS END (Away)

LONDON ROAD

EAST STAND   Disabled
SEATED ENCLOSURE

Travelling Supporters Information:
Routes: From North & West: Take A1 then A47 into Town Centre, follow Whittlesey signs across river into London Road; From East: Take A47 into Town Centre (then as North); From South: Take A1 then A15 into London Road.

PLYMOUTH ARGYLE FC

Founded: 1886
Turned Professional: 1903
Limited Company: 1903
Admitted to League: 1920
Former Name(s): Argyle FC (1886-1903)
Nickname: 'Pilgrims' 'Argyle'
Ground: Home Park, Plymouth   PL2 3DQ

Record Attendance: 43,596 (10/10/36)
Colours: Shirts - Green & Black Stripes
Shorts - Black
Telephone No.: (01752) 562561
Ticket Office: (01752) 562561
Pitch Size: 112 × 72yds
Ground Capacity: 19,900
Seating Capacity: 6,700

GENERAL INFORMATION
Supporters Club Administrator:
S. Rendell
Address: c/o Club
Telephone Number: (01752) 562561
Car Parking: Car Park (1,000 Cars) Adjacent
Coach Parking: Central Car Park
Nearest Railway Station: Plymouth North Road
Nearest Bus Station: Bretonside, Plymouth
Club Shop:
Opening Times: Monday to Saturday 9.00am - 5.00pm
Telephone No.: (01752) 558292
Postal Sales: Yes
Nearest Police Station: Devonport (1 mile)
Police Force: Devon & Cornwall
Police Telephone No.: (01752) 701188

GROUND INFORMATION
Away Supporters' Entrances: Barn Park End Turnstiles (standing)
Away Supporters' Sections: Barn Park End (Open)
Family Facilities: Location of Stand: Devonport End of Grandstand
Capacity of Stand: 600

ADMISSION INFO (1995/96 PRICES)
Adult Standing: £5.50 or £6.00
Adult Seating: £8.00 - £10.00
Child Standing: £3.50
Child Seating: £6.00
Programme Price: £1.30
FAX Number: (01752) 606167
Note: There are special rates for adults & children in the Family Enclosure (Prices shown are for category 'A' games - category 'B' & 'C' games will be at a higher price).

TAVISTOCK ROAD
LYNDHURST STAND

DEVONPORT END

BARN PARK (PEVERIL) END (Away)

GRAND STAND

Travelling Supporters Information:
Routes: From All Parts: Take A38 to Tavistock Road (A386), then branch left following signs Plymouth (A386), continue for 1.25 miles - car park on left (signposted Home Park).

PORTSMOUTH FC

Founded: 1898	**Record Attendance**: 51,385 (26/2/49)
Turned Professional: 1898	**Colours**: Shirts - Blue
Limited Company: 1898	Shorts - White
Admitted to League: 1920	**Telephone No.**: (01705) 731204
Former Name(s): None	**Ticket Office**: (01705) 750825
Nickname: 'Pompey'	**Pitch Size**: 114 × 72yds
Ground: Fratton Park, 57 Frogmore Road,	**Ground Capacity**: 26,452
Portsmouth, Hants PO4 8RA	**Seating Capacity**: 7,000

GENERAL INFORMATION
Supporters Club Administrator: -
Address: c/o Club
Telephone Number: -
Car Parking: Street Parking
Coach Parking: By Police Direction
Nearest Railway Station: Fratton (Adjacent)
Nearest Bus Station: Hilsea
Club Shop:
Opening Times: Monday to Friday 9.00am - 5.00pm. Saturdays 10.00am - 2.00pm
Telephone No.: (01705) 738358
Postal Sales: Yes
Nearest Police Station: Southsea
Police Force: Hampshire
Police Telephone No.: (01705) 321111

GROUND INFORMATION
Away Supporters' Entrances: Aspley Road - Milton Road side
Away Supporters' Sections: Aspley Road End (Open)
Family Facilities: Location of Stand:
2 - South Enclosure, Carisbrooke Road & 'G' Section, Milton Road
Capacity of Stand: 3,300 (S);   3,200 (N)

ADMISSION INFO (1995/96 PRICES)
Adult Standing: £8.00
Adult Seating: £11.00 - £15.00
Child Standing: £5.00
Child Seating: £5.00 - £7.00
Programme Price: £1.50
FAX Number: (01705) 734129

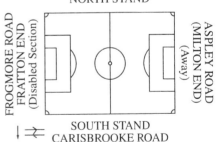

Travelling Supporters Information:
Routes: From North & West: Take M27 and M275 to end then take 2nd exit at roundabout and in 0.25 mile turn right at 'T' junction into London Road (A2047), in 1.25 mile cross railway bridge and turn left into Goldsmith Avenue. After 0.5 mile turn left into Frogmore Road; From East: Take A27 following Southsea signs (A2030). Turn left at roundabout (3 miles) into A288, then right into Priory Crescent and next right into Carisbrooke Road.

PORT VALE FC

Founded: 1876
Turned Professional: 1885
Limited Company: 1911
Admitted to League: 1892
Former Name(s): Burslem Port Vale FC (1876-1913)
Nickname: 'Valiants'
Ground: Vale Park, Burslem, Stoke-on-Trent, ST6 1AW

Record Attendance: 50,000 (20/2/60)
Colours: Shirts - White
        Shorts - Black
Telephone No.: (01782) 814134
Ticket Office: (01782) 814134
Pitch Size: 114 × 77yds
Ground Capacity: 22,359
Seating Capacity: 12,442

GENERAL INFORMATION

Supporters Club Administrator:
John Greatbatch
Address: Port Vale Supporters' Group, 90 Park Lane, Knypersley, Stoke ST8 7BQ
Telephone Number: (01782) 514721
Car Parking: Car Parks at Ground
Coach Parking: Hamil Road Car Park
Nearest Railway Station: Stoke
Nearest Bus Station: Burslem Adjacent
Club Shop:
Opening Times: Monday to Saturday 9.00am - 5.30pm
Telephone No.: (01782) 833545
Postal Sales: Yes
Nearest Police Station: Burslem
Police Force: Staffordshire
Police Telephone No.: (01782) 577114

GROUND INFORMATION

Away Supporters' Entrances: Hamil Road turnstiles
Away Supporters' Sections: Hamil Road End
Family Facilities: **Location of Stand**:
Railway Stand/Bycars Corner
Capacity of Stand: 500 seats ; 470 terracing

ADMISSION INFO (1995/96 PRICES)

Adult Standing: £6.50 - £8.00
Adult Seating: £9.00 - £10.50
Child Standing: £4.00 - £5.50
Child Seating: £5.00 - £8.00
Programme Price: £1.20
FAX Number: (01782) 834981

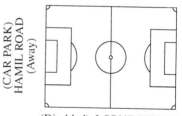

RAILWAY STAND
(Family Stand)

(CAR PARK) HAMIL ROAD
(Away)

BYCARS STAND

(Disabled) LORNE STREET
← BUS

Travelling Supporters Information:
Routes: From North: Exit M6 junction 16 and follow Stoke signs (A500). Branch left off the A500 at the exit signposted Tunstall and take 1st exit at roundabout onto A50. Turn right 0.25 mile into Newcastle Street and at end cross into Moorland Road. Turn left immediately after twin mini-roundabouts then at Traffic Lights turn left into Hamil Road. Ground is 250 yards on the right; From South & West: Exit M6 junction 15 and take A5006 and A500, after 6.25 miles branch left (then as North); From East: Take A50 or A52 into Stoke following Burslem signs into Waterloo Road, turn right at Burslem crossroads into Moorland Road (then as North).

PRESTON NORTH END FC

Founded: 1881	**Colours**: Shirts - White with Navy Trim
Turned Professional: 1885	Shorts - Blue
Limited Company: 1893	**Telephone No.**: (01772) 795919
Admitted to League: 1888	**Ticket Office**: (01772) 795919
Nickname: 'Lilywhites' 'North End'	**Pitch Size**: 110 × 72yds
Ground: Deepdale, Preston PR1 6RU	**Ground Capacity**: 10,000 Approximately
Record Attendance: 42,684 (23/4/38)	**Seating Capacity**: 1,068 (Rising to approx. 7,000 during 1996)

GENERAL INFORMATION
Supporters Club Administrator: -
Address: c/o Club
Telephone Number: -
Car Parking: West Stand Car Park (600 cars)
Coach Parking: West Stand Car Park
Nearest Railway Station: Preston (2 miles)
Nearest Bus Station: Preston (1 mile)
Club Shop:
Opening Times: Weekdays 9.00am - 5.00pm
Matchdays 12.30am - 5.00pm
Telephone No.: (01772) 795465
Postal Sales: Yes
Nearest Police Station: Lawson Street, Preston (1 mile)
Police Force: Lancashire
Police Telephone No.: (01772) 203203

GROUND INFORMATION
Away Supporters' Entrances: Pavilion Stand Turnstiles
Away Supporters' Sections: Pavilion Stand Paddock (600 places standing only)
Family Facilities: **Location of Stand**: Under development
Capacity of Stand: -

ADMISSION INFO (1995/96 PRICES)
Adult Standing: £7.00 or £7.50
Adult Seating: £10.00
Child Standing: £4.00 or £4.50
Child Seating: £6.00
Programme Price: £1.20
FAX Number: (01772) 653266

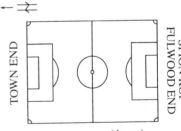

(BEING DEVELOPED)
WEST STAND

TOWN END

SPION KOP
FULWOOD END

(Away)
PAVILION STAND
LOWTHORPE ROAD

Travelling Supporters Information:
Routes: From North: M6 then M55 to junction 1. Follow signs to Preston A6. After 2 miles turn left at the crossroads into Blackpool Road (A5085). Turn right 0.75 mile into Deepdale; From South & East: Exit M6 junction 31 and follow Preston signs (A59). Take 2nd exit at roundabout (1 mile) into Blackpool Road. Turn left (1.25 mile) into Deepdale; From West: Exit M55 junction 1 (then as North).

QUEEN'S PARK RANGERS FC

Founded: 1882
Turned Professional: 1898
Limited Company: 1899
Admitted to League: 1920
Former Name(s): Formed by amalgamation of St. Jude's & Christchurch Rangers FC
Nickname: 'Rangers' 'R's'
Ground: Rangers Stadium, South Africa Road London W12 7PA

Record Attendance: 35,353 (27/4/74)
Colours: Shirts - Blue and White Hoops
Shorts - White
Telephone No.: (0181) 743-0262
Ticket Office: (0181) 749-5744
Pitch Size: 112 × 72yds
Ground Capacity: 19,200 (All Seats)

GENERAL INFORMATION

Supporters Club Administrator:
Patricia Dix
Address: c/o Club
Telephone Number: (0181) 749-6771
Car Parking: Street Parking
Coach Parking: By Police Direction
Nearest Railway Station: Shepherd's Bush
Nearest Tube Station: White City (Central)
Club Shop:
Opening Times: Monday to Friday 9.00am - 5.00pm. Saturday 9.00am - 12.30pm
Telephone No.: (0181) 749-6862
Postal Sales: Yes
Nearest Police Station: Uxbridge Road, Shepherd's Bush (0.5 mile)
Police Force: Metropolitan
Police Telephone No.: (0181) 741-6212

GROUND INFORMATION

Away Supporters' Entrances: South Africa Road, Turnstiles 29-34 & Ellerslie Road, N°s 35-37
Away Supporters' Sections: School End Stand (Partially covered)
Family Facilities: Location of Stand: Loftus Road Stand
Capacity of Stand: 3,152 seating

ADMISSION INFO (1995/96 PRICES)

Adult Seating: £8.00 - £20.00
Child Seating: £4.00 - £20.00
Programme Price: £1.50
FAX Number: (0181) 749-0994
Note: Prices vary depending on opponents. Additional concessions available for members

(Disabled)
ELLERSLIE ROAD STAND
LOFTUS ROAD STAND
(BLOEMFONTEIN ROAD)
SCHOOL END
(Away)
MAIN STAND
SOUTH AFRICA ROAD

Travelling Supporters Information:
Routes: From North: Take M1 & A406 North Circular for Neasden, turn left 0.75 mile (A404) following signs Harlesden, then Hammersmith, past White City Stadium and right into White City Road, then left into South Africa Road; From South: Take A206, A3 across Putney Bridge following signs to Hammersmith, then Oxford A219 to Shepherd's Bush to join A4020 following signs to Acton, in 0.25 mile turn right into Loftus Road; From East: Take A12, A406 then A503 to join Ring Road follow Oxford signs to join A40(M), branch left (2 miles) to M41, 3rd exit at roundabout to A4020 (then as South); From West: Take M4 to Chiswick then A315 and A402 to Shepherd's Bush, join A4020 (then as South).

READING FC

Founded: 1871
Turned Professional: 1895
Limited Company: 1897
Admitted to League: 1920
Former Name(s): Amalgamated with Hornets FC (1877) and Earley FC (1889)
Nickname: 'Royals'
Ground: Elm Park, Norfolk Road, Reading, RG3 2EF

Record Attendance: 33,042 (19/2/27)
Colours: Shirts - Blue & White
Shorts - White
Telephone No.: (01734) 507878
Ticket Office: (01734) 507878
Pitch Size: 112 × 77yds
Ground Capacity: 14,058
Seating Capacity: 2,242

GENERAL INFORMATION
Supporters Club Administrator: -
Address: -
Telephone Number: -
Car Parking: Street Parking/Prospect School /Park and Ride
Coach Parking: The Meadway
Nearest Railway Station: Reading West (0.5 mile)
Nearest Bus Station: Reading
Club Shop: Via Ticket Office
Opening Times: Monday to Friday & Matchdays 9.00am - 5.00pm
Telephone No.: (01734) 507878
Postal Sales: Yes
Nearest Police Station: Castle Street, Reading (2 miles)
Police Force: Thames Valley
Police Telephone No.: (01734) 536000

GROUND INFORMATION
Away Supporters' Entrances: Norfolk Road Turnstiles 23-29
Away Supporters' Sections: Reading End/Norfolk Road (Open Terrace) + 'A' Stand Seating
Family Facilities: Location of Stand: Norfolk Road side 'E' Stand
Capacity of Stand: 296

ADMISSION INFO (1995/96 PRICES)
Adult Standing: £8.00
Adult Seating: £9.00 - £12.00
Child Standing: £5.00 (Home fans only)
Child Seating: No Concessions
Programme Price: £1.50
FAX Number: (01734) 566628

TILEHURST ROAD
(SOUTH BANK)

SUFFOLK ROAD
READING END
(Away)

WANTAGE ROAD
TILEHURST END

NORFOLK ROAD

Travelling Supporters Information:
Routes: From North: Take A423, A4074 and A4155 from Oxford across railway bridge into Reading. Follow signs for Newbury (A4) into Castle Hill, then right into Tilehurst Road. Turn right after 0.75 mile into Cranbury Road then left and 2nd left into Norfolk Road; From South: Take A33 into Reading and follow Newbury signs into Bath Road. Cross railway bridge and take 3rd right into Liebenrood Road. At the end turn right into Tilehurst Road then 1st left into Cranbury Road and 2nd left into Norfolk Road; From East: Exit M4 junction 10 and use A329 and A4 into Reading. Cross railway bridge (then as South); From West: Exit M4 junction 12 and take A4. After 3.25 miles turn left into Liebenrood Road (then as South).

ROCHDALE FC

Founded: 1907	**Record Attendance**: 24,231 (10/12/49)
Turned Professional: 1907	**Colours**: Shirts - Blue & White
Limited Company: 1910	Shorts - Blue & White
Admitted to League: 1921	**Telephone No.**: (01706) 44648
Former Name(s): Rochdale Town FC	**Ticket Office**: (01706) 44648
Nickname: 'The Dale'	**Pitch Size**: 114 × 76yds
Ground: Willbutts Lane, Spotland, Rochdale	**Ground Capacity**: 7,564
OL11 5DS	**Seating Capacity**: 1,852

GENERAL INFORMATION
Supporters Club Administrator:
F. Duffy
Address: c/o Club
Telephone Number: (01706) 852498
Car Parking: Car Park at Ground
Coach Parking: By Police Direction
Nearest Railway Station: Rochdale (2 miles)
Nearest Bus Station: Town Centre (1 mile)
Club Shop:
Opening Times: Weekdays 9.15-5.30 and
Matchdays 9.15-6.00
Telephone No.: (01706) 47521
Postal Sales: Yes
Nearest Police Station: Rochdale (1.5 miles)
Police Force: Greater Manchester
Police Telephone No.: (01706) 47401

GROUND INFORMATION
Away Supporters' Entrances: Pearl Street Turnstiles
Away Supporters' Sections: Pearl St. End (Open & Covered)
Family Facilities: Location of Stand:
Main Stand - Blocks F & G
Capacity of Stand: 636

ADMISSION INFO (1995/96 PRICES)
Adult Standing: £6.00
Adult Seating: £8.00
Child Standing: £3.00
Child Seating: £4.50
Programme Price: £1.50
FAX Number: (01706) 48466

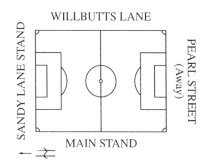

Travelling Supporters Information:
Routes: From North, South, East & West: Exit M62 junction 20 following Rochdale signs, take 2nd exit at 2nd roundabout (1.5 miles) into Roch Valley Way signed Blackburn. At next traffic lights go straight ahead and ground is on right in 0.5 miles.

ROTHERHAM UNITED FC

Founded: 1884
Turned Professional: 1905
Limited Company: 1920
Admitted to League: 1893
Former Name(s): Thornhill United FC (1884-1905); Rotherham County FC (1905-1925)
Nickname: 'The Merry Millers'
Ground: Millmoor Ground, Rotherham S60 1HR

Record Attendance: 25,000 (13/12/52)
Colours: Shirts - Red
    Shorts - White
Telephone No.: (01709) 562434
Ticket Office: (01709) 562434
Pitch Size: 115 × 76yds
Ground Capacity: 11,533
Seating Capacity: 3,407

GENERAL INFORMATION
Supporters Club Administrator: Mrs R. Cowley
Address: 50 Lister Street, Rotherham
Telephone Number: (01709) 375831
Car Parking: Kimberworth Road and Main Street Car Parks
Coach Parking: By Police Direction
Nearest Railway Station: Rotherham Central (0.5 mile)
Nearest Bus Station: Town Centre (0.5 mile)
Club Shop:
Opening Times: Monday-Friday 9.00-5.00
Telephone No.: (01709) 562760
Postal Sales: Yes
Nearest Police Station: Rotherham (0.5 mile)
Police Force: South Yorkshire
Police Telephone No.: (01709) 371121

GROUND INFORMATION
Away Supporters' Entrances: Millmoor Lane Turnstiles
Away Supporters' Sections: Millmoor Lane/Railway End
Family Facilities: Location of Stand: Millmoor Lane Side
Capacity of Stand: 748

ADMISSION INFO (1995/96 PRICES)
Adult Standing: £7.00
Adult Seating: £7.50 - £9.50
Child Standing: £4.50
Child Seating: £5.50 - £6.00
Programme Price: £1.30
FAX Number: (01709) 563336
Note: Concessions available for children with adults.

MILLMOOR LANE STAND
(Away)

MASBOROUGH STREET
TIVOLI END

RAILWAY END
(Away)

MAIN STAND

Travelling Supporters Information:
Routes: From North: Exit M1 junction 34 following Rotherham (A6109) signs to traffic lights and turn right. The Ground is 0.24 mile on right over railway bridge; From South & West: Exit M1 junction 33, turn right following 'Rotherham' signs. Turn left at roundabout and right at next roundabout. Follow dual carriageway to next roundabout and go straight on. Turn left at next roundabout and ground is 0.25 mile on left; From East: Take A630 into Rotherham following Sheffield signs. At 2nd roundabout turn right into Masborough Street then 1st left into Millmoor Lane.

SCARBOROUGH FC

Founded: 1879	**Record Attendance**: 11,124 (1938)
Limited Company: 1933	**Colours**: Shirts - Red
Admitted to League: 1987	Shorts - White
Former Name(s): None	**Telephone No.**: (01723) 375094
Nickname: 'Boro'	**Ticket Office**: (01723) 375094
Ground: McCain Stadium, Seamer Road,	**Pitch Size**: 112 × 74yds
Scarborough, N.Yorks YO12 4HF	**Ground Capacity**: 6,899
	Seating Capacity: 2,166

GENERAL INFORMATION

Social Club Administrator: Mrs.S.Nettleton
Address: c/o Club
Telephone Number: (01723) 375094
Car Parking: Street Parking
Coach Parking: Scarborough Coach Park
Nearest Railway Station: Scarborough Central (2 miles)
Nearest Bus Station: Westwood Scarborough (2 miles)
Club Shop:
Opening Times: Weekdays 9.30am - 5.00pm & Matchdays
Telephone No.: (01723) 375094
Postal Sales: Yes
Nearest Police Station: Scarborough (2 mls)
Police Force: North Yorkshire
Police Telephone No.: (01723) 500300

GROUND INFORMATION

Away Supporters' Entrances: Edgehill Road Turnstiles
Away Supporters' Sections: Visitors Enclosure, Edgehill Road End
Family Facilities: Location of Stand: None specified
Capacity of Stand: -

ADMISSION INFO (1995/96 PRICES)

Adult Standing: £6.00
Adult Seating: £8.50
Child Standing: £3.50
Child Seating: £6.00
Programme Price: £1.00
FAX Number: (01723) 378733

```
          CAR PARK
        McCAIN STAND

  SEAMER ROAD            EDGEHILL ROAD
  EAST STAND               (Away)

          MAIN STAND
```

Travelling Supporters Information:
Routes: The Ground is situated on the main York to Scarborough Road (A64) 0.5 mile on left past B & Q DIY Store.

SCUNTHORPE UNITED FC

Founded: 1899
Turned Professional: 1912
Limited Company: 1912
Admitted to League: 1950
Former Name(s): Scunthorpe & Lindsey United (1899-1912)
Nickname: 'Irons'
Ground: Glanford Park, Doncaster Road, Scunthorpe, South Humberside DN15 8TD

Record Attendance: 8,775 (1/5/89)
Colours: Shirts - White with Claret/Blue Trim
Shorts - Sky Blue + Claret/Blue Trim
Telephone No.: (01724) 848077
Ticket Office: (01724) 848077
Pitch Size: 111 × 73yds
Ground Capacity: 9,200
Seating Capacity: 6,400

GENERAL INFORMATION
Supporters Club Administrator:
A. Webster
Address: 12 Byfield Road, Scunthorpe
Telephone Number: (01724) 863009
Car Parking: For 600 cars at Ground
Coach Parking: At Ground
Nearest Railway Station: Scunthorpe (1.5 miles)
Nearest Bus Station: Scunthorpe (1.5 miles)
Club Shop: (Club Offices)
Opening Times: Weekdays 9.00am - 5.00pm
Matchdays 10.30am - 3.00pm & 4.45-5.15pm
Telephone No.: (01724) 848077
Postal Sales: Yes
Nearest Police Station: Laneham Street, Scunthorpe (1.5 miles)
Police Force: Humberside
Police Telephone No.: (01724) 282888

GROUND INFORMATION
Away Supporters' Entrances: Turnstiles 6-7
Away Supporters' Sections: South Stand
Family Facilities: Location of Stand: Clugston Stand
Capacity of Stand: 2,277

ADMISSION INFO (1995/96 PRICES)
Adult Standing: £6.00
Adult Seating: £7.50 - £8.50
Child Standing: £3.00
Child Seating: £3.70 or £5.50
Programme Price: £1.30
FAX Number: (01724) 857986

CLUGSTON STAND
(Disabled)

BRITISH STEEL STAND

YORKSHIRE ELECTRICITY STAND
(Away)

SCUNTHORPE EVENING TELEGRAPH STAND

Travelling Supporters Information:
Routes: From All Parts: Exit M180 junction 3 onto M181. Follow M181 to roundabout with A18 and take A18 towards Scunthorpe - Ground on right next to roundabout (200 yards).

SHEFFIELD UNITED FC

Founded: 1889
Turned Professional: 1889
Limited Company: 1899
Admitted to League: 1892
Former Name(s): None
Nickname: 'Blades'
Ground: Bramall Lane, Sheffield   S2 4SU

Record Attendance: 68,287 (15/2/36)
Colours: Shirts - Red & White Stripes with
Black Pinstripe
Shorts - Black
Telephone No.: (0114) 273-8955
Ticket Office: (0114) 276-6771
Pitch Size: 112 × 72yds
Ground Capacity: 23,459 (All Seats)

GENERAL INFORMATION
Supporters Club Administrator:
Beryl Whitney
Address: 42 Base Green Avenue, Sheffield
S12 3FA
Telephone Number: (0114) 239-0202
Car Parking: Street Parking
Coach Parking: By Police Direction
Nearest Railway Station: Sheffield Midland
(1 mile)
Nearest Bus Station: Pond Street, Sheffield
Club Shop:
Opening Times: Monday-Friday 9.30am -
5.00pm & Matchdays 9.30am - 5.30pm
Telephone No.: (0114) 275-0596
Postal Sales: Yes
Nearest Police Station: Police Room at
Ground
Police Force: South Yorkshire
Police Telephone No.: (0114) 276-8522

GROUND INFORMATION
Away Supporters' Entrances: Bramall Lane
Turnstiles
Away Supporters' Sections: Bramall Lane Upper
Stand
Family Facilities: Location of Stand:
South Stand - West Wing - Membership Area
Capacity of Stand: 2,000 (Family Section)
ADMISSION INFO (1995/96 PRICES)
Adult Seating: £9.00 - £14.00
Child Seating: £6.00 - £7.00
Programme Price: £1.50
FAX Number: (0114) 272-3030

CHERRY STREET
SOUTH STAND

SHOREHAM STREET
KOP SEATS

BRAMALL LANE
UPPER (Away)
LOWER (Home)

JOHN STREET
(UNDER DEVELOPMENT)

Travelling Supporters Information:
Routes: From North: Exit M1 junction 34 following signs to Sheffield (A6109), turn left 3.5 miles and take
4th exit at roundabout into Sheaf Street. Take 5th exit at 2nd roundabout into St. Mary's Road (for Bakewell),
turn left 0.5 mile into Bramall Lane; From South & East: Exit M1 junctions 31 or 33 and take A57 to roundabout, take 3rd exit into Sheaf Street (then as North); From West: Take A57 into Sheffield and take 4th exit
at roundabout into Upper Hanover Street and at 2nd roundabout take 3rd exit into Bramall Lane.

SHEFFIELD WEDNESDAY FC

Founded: 1867	**Record Attendance**: 72,841 (17/2/34)
Turned Professional: 1887	**Colours**: Shirts - Blue & White Stripes
Limited Company: 1899	Shorts - Black
Admitted to League: 1892	**Telephone No.**: (0114) 234-3122
Former Name(s): The Wednesday FC	**Ticket Office**: (0114) 233-7233
Nickname: 'Owls'	**Pitch Size**: 115 × 75yds
Ground: Hillsborough, Sheffield S6 1SW	**Ground Capacity**: 36,020 (All Seats)

GENERAL INFORMATION
Supporters Club Administrator: -
Address: -
Telephone Number: -
Car Parking: Street Parking
Coach Parking: Owlerton Stadium
Nearest Railway Station: Sheffield (4 miles)
Nearest Bus Station: Sheffield (4 miles)
Club Shop:
Opening Times: Monday-Saturday
10.00-4.30
Telephone No.: (0114) 234-3342
Postal Sales: Yes
Nearest Police Station: Hammerton Road,
Sheffield (1 mile)
Police Force: South Yorkshire
Police Telephone No.: (0114) 234-3131

GROUND INFORMATION
Away Supporters' Entrances: West Stand Turnstiles
Away Supporters' Sections: West Stand - Lower Tier
Family Facilities: Location of Stand:
Penistone Road Wing
Capacity of Stand: Approximately 1,000
ADMISSION INFO (1995/96 PRICES)
Adult Seating: £8.50 - £17.00
Child Seating: £5.00 - £11.50
Programme Price: £1.30
FAX Number: (0114) 233-7145
(Prices depend on category of game)

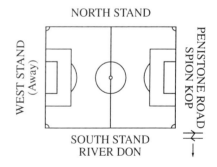

Travelling Supporters Information:
Routes: From North: Exit M1 junction 34 following signs for Sheffield (A6109), take 3rd exit (1.5 miles) at roundabout and in 3.25 miles turn left into Herries Road for Ground; From South & East: Exit M1 junctions 31 or 33 and take A57 to roundabout, take exit into Prince of Wales Road after 5.75 miles turn left into Herries Road South; From West: Take A57 until A6101 and turn left. After 3.75 miles turn left at 'T' junction into Penistone Road for Ground.

SHREWSBURY TOWN FC

Founded: 1886	**Record Attendance**: 18,917 (26/4/61)
Turned Professional: 1905	**Colours**: Shirts - Blue, Yellow & White
Limited Company: 1936	Shorts - Blue, Yellow & White
Admitted to League: 1950	**Telephone No.**: (01743) 360111
Former Name(s): None	**Ticket Office**: (01743) 360111
Nickname: 'Town'	**Pitch Size**: 116 × 75yds
Ground: Gay Meadow, Shrewsbury	**Ground Capacity**: 8,000
SY2 6AB	**Seating Capacity**: 3,000

GENERAL INFORMATION

Supporters Club Administrator:
Peter Sandford
Address: c/o Club
Telephone Number: (01743) 360111
Car Parking: Car Park Adjacent
Coach Parking: Gay Meadow
Nearest Railway Station: Shrewsbury
(1 mile)
Nearest Bus Station: Baker Street,
Shrewsbury
Club Shop:
Opening Times: Matchdays & Office Hours
Telephone No.: (01743) 356316
Postal Sales: Yes
Nearest Police Station: Clive Road,
Shrewsbury
Police Force: West Mercia
Police Telephone No.: (01743) 232888

GROUND INFORMATION

Away Supporters' Entrances: Station End Turnstiles
Away Supporters' Sections: Station Stand (Covered)
Family Facilities: **Location of Stand**:
Wakeman Stand
Capacity of Stand: 500

ADMISSION INFO (1995/96 PRICES)

Adult Standing: £7.00
Adult Seating: £9.00 - £10.00 (Members only)
Child Standing: £4.00 (Members only)
Child Seating: £5.00 (Wakeman Stand)
Away Standing: £7.00 (No concessions)
Away Seating: £10.00 (No concessions)
Programme Price: £1.30
FAX Number: (01743) 236384

```
        STATION  CENTRE  WAKEMAN
         STAND    STAND    STAND
(Away)
                                    A
  (CAR PARK)                        B
  STATION END                       B
                                    E
                                    Y
                                    F
                                    O
                                    R
                                    E
                                    G
                                    A
                                    T
                                    E
         RIVERSIDE ENCLOSURE
           (RIVER SEVERN)
```

Travelling Supporters Information:

Routes: From North: Take A49 or A53 then 2nd exit at roundabout into Telford Way (A5112). After 0.75 mile take 2nd exit at roundabout. Turn right at 'T' junction into Abbey Foregate for Ground; From South: Take A49 to Town Centre and at end of Coleham Head, turn right into Abbey Foregate; From East: Take A5 then A458 into Town Centre straight forward to Abbey Foregate; From West: Take A458 then A5 around Ring Road, Roman Road, then turn left into Hereford Road and at end of Coleman Head turn right into Abbey Foregate.

SOUTHAMPTON FC

Founded: 1885
Turned Professional: 1894
Limited Company: 1897
Admitted to League: 1920
Former Name(s): Southampton St.Mary's YMCA FC (1885-1897)
Nickname: 'Saints'
Ground: The Dell, Milton Road, Southampton SO9 4XX

Record Attendance: 31,044 (8/10/69)
Colours: Shirts - Red & White
　　　　　 Shorts - Black
Telephone No.: (01703) 220505
Pitch Size: 110 × 72yds
Ground Capacity: 15,000 (All Seats)

GENERAL INFORMATION

Supporters Club Administrator:
The Secretary
Address: Saints Supporters' Social Club, The Dell, Milton Road, Southampton
Telephone Number: (01703) 336450
Car Parking: Street Parking
Coach Parking: By Police Direction
Nearest Railway Station: Southampton Central (1 mile)
Nearest Bus Station: West Quay Road by Centre 2000
Club Shop:
Opening Times: Monday-Saturday 9.00am - 5.00pm (closed Wednesday)
Telephone No.: (01703) 236400
Postal Sales: Yes
Nearest Police Station: Civic Centre, Southampton (1 mile)
Police Force: Hampshire
Police Telephone No.: (01703) 581111

GROUND INFORMATION

Away Supporters' Entrances: Archers Road Turnstiles 16-20
Away Supporters' Sections: Upper/Lower East Stand Archers Road End
Family Facilities:　**Location of Stand**: West Stand - Lower Seats
Capacity of Stand: 1,282

ADMISSION INFO (1994/95 PRICES)

Adult Seating: £11.00 - £14.00/£13.00 - £16.00
Child Seating: £5 or £6 - Lower East/West Stand Only
Programme Price: £1.50
FAX Number: (01703) 330360
Note: Matches are split into Categories of 'Silver' and 'Gold'. Prices shown to the left of the / are Silver

```
                    EAST STAND
        (Away)
  A                                        W M
  R                                        I I
  C                                        L L
  H                                        T T
  E                                        O O
  R                                        N N
  S                                        A R
                                           V O
  R                                        E A
  O                                        N D
  A                                        U
  D                                        E
  E               Blind
  N                        Wheelchairs
  D          WEST STAND
        HILL LANE/MILTON ROAD
```

Travelling Supporters Information:
Routes: From North: Take A33 into the Avenue and turn right into Northlands Road. Turn right at end into Archer's Road; From East: Take M27 to A334 and follow signs Southampton A3024. Then follow signs The West into Commercial Road, turn right into Hill Lane then 1st right into Milton Road; From West: Take A35 then A3024 following signs City Centre into Fourposts Hill then left into Hill Lane and 1st right into Milton Road.

SOUTHEND UNITED FC

Founded: 1906	**Record Attendance**: 31,033 (10/1/79)
Turned Professional: 1906	**Colours**: Shirts - Blue and Red
Limited Company: 1919	Shorts - Blue and Red
Admitted to League: 1920	**Telephone No.**: (01702) 340707
Former Name(s): Southend Athletic FC	**Ticket Office**: (01702) 435602
Nickname: 'Shrimpers' 'Blues'	**Pitch Size**: 110 × 74yds
Ground: Roots Hall Ground, Victoria Avenue, Southend-on-Sea SS2 6NQ	**Ground Capacity**: 10,350 (All Seats)

GENERAL INFORMATION
Supporters Club Secretary: Tony Walters
Address: c/o Club
Telephone Number: (01702) 340707
Car Parking: Car Park at Ground (500 cars)
- Season Ticket Holders Only + Street Parking
Coach Parking: Car Park
Nearest Railway Station: Prittlewell (0.5 ml)
Nearest Bus Station: London Road, Southend
Club Shop: At Ground and in Town
Opening Times: Ground: - Weekdays &
Matchdays 10.30-4.30pm (except Mondays &
Wednesdays); Town: - Monday-Saturday
9.30-5.00pm
Telephone No.: (01702) 435067(Ground);
(01702) 601351 (Town).
Postal Sales: Yes
Nearest Police Station: Southend-on-Sea
(0.25 mile)
Police Force: Essex
Police Telephone No.: (01702) 431212

GROUND INFORMATION
Away Supporters' Entrances: North Stand Turnstiles
Away Supporters' Sections: North Stand
Family Facilities: Location of Stand:
West Stand
Capacity of Stand: 3,045

ADMISSION INFO (1995/96 PRICES)
Adult Seating: £12.00 - £15.00
Child Seating: £5.00 (Members)
Away Seating: £10.00 (No Concessions)
Programme Price: £1.40
FAX Number: (01702) 330164
Note: Concessions only available for members.

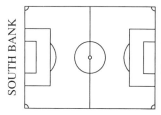

SHAKESPEARE DRIVE
WEST STAND
SOUTH BANK
FAIRFAX DRIVE
NORTH STAND
(Away)
EAST STAND
VICTORIA AVENUE

Travelling Supporters Information:
Routes: From North & West: Take A127 into Southend then at roundabout take 3rd exit into Victoria Avenue; From South: Take A13 following signs for Southend and turn left into West Road. At the end of West Road turn left into Victoria Avenue.

STOCKPORT COUNTY FC

Founded: 1883
Turned Professional: 1891
Limited Company: 1908
Admitted to League: 1900
Former Name(s): Heaton Norris Rovers FC;
Heaton Norris FC
Nickname: 'Hatters' 'County'
Ground: Edgeley Park, Hardcastle Road,
Edgeley, Stockport SK3 9DD

Record Attendance: 27,833 (11/2/50)
Colours: Shirts - Blue with Red & Blue Flashes
Shorts - White
Telephone No.: (0161) 480-8888
Ticket Office: (0161) 480-8888
Pitch Size: 111 × 71yds
Ground Capacity: 9,310 (All Seats)

GENERAL INFORMATION
Supporters Club Administrator:
Ken Boxshall
Address: c/o Club Shop
Telephone Number: (0161) 480-8117
Car Parking: Street Parking
Coach Parking: By Police Direction
Nearest Railway Station: Stockport
(5 minutes walk)
Nearest Bus Station: Mersey Square
(10 minutes walk)
Club Shop:
Opening Times: Weekdays 9.00-5.00pm
Saturdays 9.30-12.30pm
Telephone No.: (0161) 480-8117
Postal Sales: Yes
Nearest Police Station: Stockport (1 mile)
Police Force: Greater Manchester
Police Telephone No.: (0161) 872-5050

GROUND INFORMATION
Away Supporters' Entrances: Railway End Turnstiles
Away Supporters' Sections: Railway End & Main
Stand
Family Facilities: **Location of Stand**:
In front of Main Stand & Barlow Stand
Capacity of Stand: 1,800

ADMISSION INFO (1995/96 PRICES)
Adult Seating: £7.00 - £9.00
Child Seating: £3.00
Away Fans: All priced £7.00 (No concessions)
Programme Price: £1.30
FAX Number: (0161) 480-0230

POPULAR SIDE

RAILWAY END
(Away)

CHEADLE END

MAIN STAND
HARDCASTLE ROAD

Travelling Supporters Information:
Routes: From North, South & West: Exit M63 junction 11 and join A560, following signs for Cheadle,
after 0.25 mile turn right into Edgeley Road and in 1 mile turn right into Caroline Street for Ground; From
East: Take A6 or A560 into Stockport Town Centre and turn left into Greek Street. Take 2nd exit into
Mercian Way (from roundabout) then turn left into Caroline Street - Ground straight ahead.

STOKE CITY FC

Founded: 1863	**Record Attendance**: 51,380 (29/3/37)
Turned Professional: 1885	**Colours**: Shirts - Red & White Stripes
Limited Company: 1908	Shorts - White
Admitted to League: 1888 (Founder)	**Telephone No.**: (01782) 413511
Former Name(s): Stoke FC	**Ticket Office**: (01782) 413961
Nickname: 'Potters'	**Pitch Size**: 116 × 72yds
Ground: Victoria Ground, Boothen Old Road,	**Ground Capacity**: 25,084
Stoke-on-Trent ST4 4EG	**Seating Capacity**: 9,625

GENERAL INFORMATION
Supporters Club Administrator:
Nic Mansfield
Address: 11A Westland Street, Penkhull,
Stoke-on-Trent   ST4   7HE
Telephone Number: (01782) 744674
Car Parking: Car Park at Ground (2,000 cars)
Coach Parking: Whieldon Road
Nearest Railway Station: Stoke-on-Trent
(10 minutes walk)
Nearest Bus Station: Hanley (2 miles)
Club Shop:
Opening Times: Monday to Friday 9.30-5.00
Saturdays 9.30-12.00
Telephone No.: (01782) 747078
Postal Sales: Yes
Nearest Police Station: Stoke-on-Trent
(0.25 mile)
Police Force: Staffordshire
Police Telephone No.: (01782) 744644

GROUND INFORMATION
Away Supporters' Entrances: Butler Street
Turnstiles 47-49, Stoke End 33-35/41-46
Away Supporters' Sections: Butler Street Stand &
Block A Stoke End Paddock
Family Facilities: Location of Stand:
Stoke End Stand
Capacity of Stand: 2,000

ADMISSION INFO (1995/96 PRICES)
Adult Standing: £8.00
Adult Seating: £12.00
Child Standing: £5.00
Child Seating: £6.00
Programme Price: £1.50
FAX Number: (01782) 46422

```
                    (CAR PARK)
                   BUTLER STREET
                      (Away)

  LONSDALE STREET                    BOOTHEN END
  STOKE END

              BOOTHEN STAND
              BOOTHEN OLD ROAD
```

Travelling Supporters Information:
Routes: From North, South & West: Exit M6 junction 15 and follow signs Stoke (A5006) and join A500.
Branch left 0.75 mile and take 2nd exit at roundabout into Campbell Road for Ground; From East: Take
A50 into Stoke Town Centre and turn left at crossroads into Lonsdale Street for Campbell Road.

SUNDERLAND AFC

Founded: 1879
Turned Professional: 1886
Limited Company: 1906
Admitted to League: 1890
Former Name(s): Sunderland & District Teachers FC
Nickname: 'Rokerites'
Ground: Roker Park, Grantham Road, Roker Sunderland   SR6 9SW

Record Attendance: 75,118 (8/3/33)
Colours: Shirts - Red & White Stripes
Shorts - Black
Telephone No.: (0191) 514-0332
Ticket Office: (0191) 514-0332
Pitch Size: 113 × 74yds
Ground Capacity: 22,657
Seating Capacity: 7,753

GENERAL INFORMATION
Supporters Club Administrator: Audrey Baillie
Address: 36 Roker Baths Road, Roker, Sunderland
Telephone Number: (0191) 567-0067
Car Parking: Car Park for 1,500 cars
Coach Parking: Seafront, Roker
Nearest Railway Station: Seaburn
Nearest Bus Station: Town Centre (2 miles)
Club Shop: Town Centre & Roker Park
Opening Times: Monday-Saturday 9.00-5.00
Telephone No.: (0191) 564-0002
Postal Sales: Yes
Nearest Police Station: Southwick (1.25 ml)
Police Force: Northumbria
Police Telephone No.: (0191) 510-2020

GROUND INFORMATION
Away Supporters' Entrances: Roker End Turnstiles
Away Supporters' Sections: Roker End
Family Facilities: **Location of Stand**: Centre Stand
Capacity of Stand: 514

ADMISSION INFO (1995/96 PRICES)
Adult Standing: £10 Members   £11 Non-members
Adult Seating: £13.00 - £15.00
Child Standing: £6.00
Child Seating: £13.00   (Family Enclosure £8.00)
Programme Price: £1.30
FAX Number: (0191) 514-5854

Travelling Supporters Information:
Routes: Take A19 to Sunderland. Take A1231 turn-off for Sunderland North and follow the signs to the City Centre. After 2 miles, at traffic lights, go straight ahead in the left lane marked A1289 to Roker. After 1 mile, follow the Roker A183 signs. 200 yards after that follow signs for Whitburn & Sea Front (A183) and after 0.5 mile turn left down side street, the football ground is straight ahead.

SWANSEA CITY FC

Founded: 1900	**Record Attendance**: 32,796 (17/2/68)
Turned Professional: 1912	**Colours**: Shirts - White
Limited Company: 1912	Shorts - White
Admitted to League: 1920	**Telephone No.**: (01792) 474114
Former Name(s): Swansea Town FC	**Ticket Office**: (01792) 474114
(1900-1970)	**Pitch Size**: 110 × 74yds
Nickname: 'Swans'	**Ground Capacity**: 16,499
Ground: Vetch Field, Swansea SA1 3SU	**Seating Capacity**: 3,414

GENERAL INFORMATION
Supporters Club Administrator:
John Button
Address: 159 Western Street, Swansea
Telephone Number: (01792) 460958
Car Parking: Kingsway Car Park (200 yards)
& Clarence Terrace Car Park (50 yards) and
Street Parking
Coach Parking: By Police Direction
Nearest Railway Station: Swansea High
Street (1 mile)
Nearest Bus Station: Quadrant Depot
(0.25 mile)
Club Shop: 33 William Street, Swansea
SA1 3QS
Opening Times: Weekdays 10.00-4.30
Matchdays 9.30-5.00
Telephone No.: (01792) 462584
Postal Sales: Yes
Nearest Police Station: Swansea Central
(1 mile)
Police Force: South Wales
Police Telephone No.: (01792) 456999

GROUND INFORMATION
Away Supporters' Entrances: Richardson Street
Turnstiles
Away Supporters' Sections: West Terrace Enclosure
- Partially covered
Family Facilities: Location of Stand:
Jewson Family Enclosure (West Side of Centre Stand)
Capacity of Stand: 321 seats

ADMISSION INFO (1995/96 PRICES)
Adult Standing: £7.50
Adult Seating: £9.00 - £11.00
Child Standing: £4.00
Child Seating: Family + 1 = £14.00   + 2 = £16.00
Programme Price: £1.30
FAX Number: (01792) 646120

Travelling Supporters Information:

Routes: From All Parts: Exit M4 at Junction 42 and follow Swansea (A483) signs. After 4 miles follow signs for City Centre West. After 0.5 mile turn right (opposite County Hall) into West Way. At first set of Traffic Lights, turn left into Glamorgan Street for Vetch Field.

SWINDON TOWN FC

Founded: 1881
Turned Professional: 1895
Limited Company: 1897
Admitted to League: 1920
Former Name(s): None
Nickname: 'Robins'
Ground: County Ground, County Road,
Swindon   SN1 2ED

Record Attendance: 32,000 (15/1/72)
Colours: Shirts - Red
         Shorts - Red
Telephone No.: (01793) 430430
Ticket Office: (01793) 529000
Pitch Size: 114 × 74yds
Ground Capacity: 15,341 (All Seats))

GENERAL INFORMATION
Supporters Club Administrator:
Miss S.Cobern
Address: 31 Pewsham Road, Penhill,
Swindon
Telephone Number: (01793) 481061
Car Parking: Town Centre
Coach Parking: Car Park Adjacent
Nearest Railway Station: Swindon (0.5 mile)
Nearest Bus Station: Swindon (0.5 mile)
Club Shop: The Swindon Town Superstore
Opening Times: Weekdays 9.00am - 5.00pm
Saturdays 9.00-3.00pm on matchdays only
Telephone No.: (01793) 423030
Postal Sales: Yes
Nearest Police Station: Fleming Way,
Swindon
Police Force: Wiltshire
Police Telephone No.: (01793) 528111

GROUND INFORMATION
Away Supporters' Entrances: Intel Stand
Away Supporters' Sections: Intel Stand
Family Facilities: Location of Stand:
Town End Stand
Capacity of Stand: 1,950
ADMISSION INFO (1995/96 PRICES)
Adult Seating: £9.00 - £12.50
Child Seating: £4.50 - £7.00
Programme Price: £1.50
FAX Number: (01793) 536170

NORTH STAND

COUNTY ROAD
TOWN END

STRATTON BANK

(Away)
INTEL STAND

Travelling Supporters Information:
Routes: From London & East & South: Exit M4 junction 15 and take A345 into Swindon along Queen's
Drive, take 3rd exit at 'Magic Roundabout' into County Road; From West: Exit M4 junction 15 then as
above; From North: Take M4 or A345/A420/A361 to County Road roundabout then as above.

TORQUAY UNITED FC

Founded: 1898
Turned Professional: 1921
Limited Company: 1921
Admitted to League: 1927
Former Name(s): Torquay Town (1898-1910)
Nickname: 'Gulls'
Ground: Plainmoor Ground, Torquay
TQ1 3PS

Record Attendance: 21,908 (29/1/55)
Colours: Shirts - Yellow, Navy & White Stripes
Shorts - Navy
Telephone No.: (01803) 328666
Ticket Office: (01803) 328666
Pitch Size: 110 × 74yds
Ground Capacity: 5,987
Seating Capacity: 2,324

GENERAL INFORMATION
Supporters Club Chairman: Mr. T. Webb
Address: 50 Carlton Road, Torquay
Telephone Number: (01803) 297778
Car Parking: Street Parking
Coach Parking: Lymington Road Coach
Station (0.5 mile)
Nearest Railway Station: Torquay (2 miles)
Nearest Bus Station: Lymington Road
(0.5 mile)
Club Shop:
Opening Times: Matchdays & During Office
Hours
Telephone No.: (01803) 328666
Postal Sales: Yes
Nearest Police Station: Torquay (1 mile)
Police Force: Devon & Cornwall
Police Telephone No.: (01803) 214491

GROUND INFORMATION
Away Supporters' Entrances: Babbacombe End
Turnstiles
Away Supporters' Sections: Babbacombe End
Family Facilities: **Location of Stand**:
Ellacombe End
Capacity of Stand: 1,370

ADMISSION INFO (1995/96 PRICES)
Adult Standing: £4.00 - £8.00
Adult Seating: £4.00 - £8.00
Child Standing: £1.00 - £5.00
Child Seating: £1.00 - £5.00
Programme Price: £1.30
FAX Number: (01803) 323976
(Matches categorised & prices vary for each category)

(GRAND STAND)
HOMELANDS LANE

WARBRO ROAD
BABBACOMBE END
(Away)

ELLACOMBE END

MARNHAM ROAD
POPULAR SIDE

Travelling Supporters Information:
Routes: From North & East: Take M5 to A38 and A380 to Torquay. On entering Torquay, turn left at the
3rd set of Traffic Lights into Hele Road. Continue straight on over two mini-roundabouts and up West Hill
Road to Traffic Lights, then go straight ahead into Warbro Road. The Ground is situated 200 yards on the
right.

TOTTENHAM HOTSPUR FC

Founded: 1882
Turned Professional: 1895
Limited Company: 1898
Admitted to League: 1908
Former Name(s): Hotspur FC (1882-85)
Nickname: 'Spurs'
Ground: White Hart Lane, 748 High Road, Tottenham, London N17 0AP

Record Attendance: 75,038 (5/3/38)
Colours: Shirts - White
Shorts - Navy Blue
Telephone No.: (0181) 365-5000
Ticket Office: (0181) 365-5050
Pitch Size: 110 × 73yds
Ground Capacity: 33,147 (All Seats)

GENERAL INFORMATION
Supporters Club Administrator:
Linda Watkins
Address: Spurs Members Club, 752B High Road, Tottenham N17
Telephone Number: (0181) 365-5150
Car Parking: None within 0.25 mile
Coach Parking: Northumberland Park Coach Park
Nearest Railway Station: White Hart Lane (Nearby)/Northumberland Park
Nearest Tube Station: Seven Sisters (Victoria); Manor House (Piccadilly)
Club Shop:
Opening Times: Weekdays 9.30-5.30 and Matchdays 9.30-6.00
Telephone No.: (0181) 880-9019
Postal Sales: Yes
Nearest Police Station: Tottenham (1 mile)
Police Force: Metropolitan
Police Telephone No.: (0181) 801-3443

GROUND INFORMATION
Away Supporters' Entrances: Park Lane
Away Supporters' Sections: South Stand, Park Lane
Family Facilities: **Location of Stand**:
Members Stand
Capacity of Stand: 6,932

ADMISSION INFO (1994/95 PRICES)
Adult Seating: £13 - £35 (Members £12 - £16)
Child Seating: Members Only £6.00 - £8.50
Programme Price: £1.50
FAX Number: (0181) 365-5005

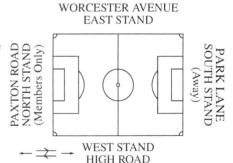

Travelling Supporters Information:
Routes: From All Parts: Take A406 North Circular to Edmonton and at traffic lights follow signs for Tottenham (A1010) into Fore Street for Ground.

TRANMERE ROVERS FC

Founded: 1881
Turned Professional: 1912
Limited Company: 1920
Admitted to League: 1921
Former Name(s): Belmont FC
Nickname: 'Rovers'
Ground: Prenton Park, Prenton Road West, Birkenhead   L42 9PN

Record Attendance: 24,424 (5/2/72)
Colours: Shirts - White
    Shorts - White
Telephone No.: (0151) 608-3677
Ticket Office: (0151) 608-3677
Pitch Size: 110 × 70yds
Ground Capacity: 16,800 (All Seats)

GENERAL INFORMATION
Supporters Club Administrator: C. Dalziel
Address: c/o Club
Telephone Number: (0151) 608-3677
Car Parking: Large Car Park at Ground
Coach Parking: At Ground
Nearest Railway Station: Hamilton Square, Rock Ferry (1 mile)
Nearest Bus Station: Birkenhead
Club Shop:
Opening Times: Weekdays & Matchdays 9.00-5.00
Telephone No.: (0151) 608-0438
Postal Sales: Yes
Nearest Police Station: Bebington (2 miles)
Police Force: Merseyside
Police Telephone No.: (0151) 709-6010

GROUND INFORMATION
Away Supporters' Entrances: Kop Stand Turnstiles - access from Main Car Park
Away Supporters' Sections: Kop Stand
Family Facilities: Location of Stand: Family Enclosure
Capacity of Stand: 3,800

ADMISSION INFO (1995/96 PRICES)
Adult Seating: £8.00-£10.50
Programme Price: £1.20
FAX Number: (0151) 608-4385
Note: Concessionary admission by prepaid vouchers (available in books of 5 for £15.00)

MAIN STAND
(FAMILY STAND)
(Disabled)

KOP STAND
(Away)

COWSHED STAND

BOROUGH ROAD STAND

Travelling Supporters Information:
Routes: From North: Take Mersey Tunnel to M53, exit junction 3 and take 1st exit at roundabout (A552), in 1.25 mile turn right at crossroads (B5151) then left into Prenton Road West; From South & East: Exit M53 junction 4 and take 4th exit at roundabout (B5151). After 2.5 miles turn right into Prenton Road West.

WALSALL FC

Founded: 1888
Turned Professional: 1888
Limited Company: 1921
Admitted to League: 1892
Former Name(s): Walsall Town Swifts FC (1888-95)
Nickname: 'Saddlers'
Ground: Bescot Stadium, Bescot Crescent, Walsall, West Midlands WS1 4SA

Record Attendance: 10,628 (20/5/91)
(England B vs. Switzerland)
Colours: Shirts - Red & White Stripes
Shorts - Black
Telephone No.: (01922) 22791
Ticket Information: (01922) 22791
Pitch Size: 110 × 73yds
Ground Capacity: 9,485
Seating Capacity: 6,685

GENERAL INFORMATION

Supporters Club Administrator: John Wilson
Address: Saddlers Club, Wallows Lane, Walsall
Telephone Number: (01922) 22257
Car Parking: Car Park at Ground
Coach Parking: At Ground
Nearest Railway Station: Bescot (Adjacent)
Nearest Bus Station: Bradford Place, Walsall
Bus Services to Ground: 2/312/323/636/637
Specials: 977/978/979/980/981
Club Shop:
Opening Times: Weekdays 10.00-2.00pm and Matchdays 9.30-5.15pm
Telephone No.: (01922) 643331
Postal Sales: Yes
Nearest Police Station: Walsall (2 miles)
Police Force: West Midlands
Police Telephone No.: (01922) 38111

GROUND INFORMATION

Away Supporters' Entrances: Highgate Stand Turnstiles 1-4
Away Supporters' Sections: Highgate Stand
Family Facilities: **Location of Stand**:
In front of Highgate Stand - Blocks A & B
Capacity of Stand: 800 Seats

ADMISSION INFO (1995/96 PRICES)

Adult Standing: £7.00
Adult Seating: £9.00 - £10.00
Child Standing: £5.00
Child Seating: £5.00 - £9.00
Programme Price: £1.20
FAX Number: (01922) 613202

HIGHGATE STAND
(Away)

GILBERT ALSO STAND

(BESCOT CRESCENT)
WILLIAM SHARP STAND

H.L. FELLOWS STAND

Travelling Supporters Information:
Routes: From All Parts: Exit M6 junction 9 turning North towards Walsall onto the A461. After 0.25 mile turn right into Wallows Lane and pass over Railway Bridge. Then take 1st right into Bescot Crescent and ground is 0.5 mile along on left adjacent to Bescot Railway Station.

WATFORD FC

Founded: 1891
Turned Professional: 1897
Limited Company: 1909
Admitted to League: 1920
Former Name(s): Formed by Amalgamation of West Herts FC & St Mary's FC
Nickname: 'Hornets'
Ground: Vicarage Road Stadium, Watford WD1 8ER

Record Attendance: 34,099 (3/2/69)
Colours: Shirts - Yellow with Black & Red Shorts - Black
Telephone No.: (01923) 230933
Ticket Office: (01923) 230933
Pitch Size: 115 × 75yds
Ground Capacity: 22,000 (All Seats)

GENERAL INFORMATION
Supporters Club Administrator: c/o Marketing Department
Address: c/o Club
Telephone Number: (01923) 225761
Car Parking: Nearby Multi-Storey Car Park
Coach Parking: Cardiff Road Car Park
Nearest Railway Station: Station at Ground (for Big Games only) or Watford Junction
Nearest Bus Station: Watford
Club Shop:
Opening Times: Monday to Saturday 9.00-5.00
Telephone No.: (01923) 220847
Postal Sales: Yes
Nearest Police Station: Shady Lane, Clarendon Road, Watford (1.5 miles)
Police Force: Hertfordshire
Police Telephone No.: (01923) 244444

GROUND INFORMATION
Away Supporters' Entrances: South West Corner
Away Supporters' Sections: Rous Stand Lower Tier
Family Facilities: **Location of Stand**: Family Block (Season Ticket holders only)
Capacity of Stand: 750 Seated in Family Block

ADMISSION INFO (1995/96 PRICES)
Adult Seating: £11.00 or £13.00
Child Seating: £8.00 or £13.00
Programme Price: £1.50
FAX Number: (01923) 239759

(Away)   ROUS STAND

SOUTH STAND

VICARAGE ROAD
NORTH STAND
(HOME FANS ONLY)

(FAMILY ENCLOSURE)
OCCUPATION ROAD
EAST STAND

Travelling Supporters Information:
Routes: From North: Exit M1 junction 5 take 2nd exit at roundabout, A41 signposted Harrow. Take 3rd exit at next roundabout to Hartspring Lane. Follow through traffic lights and continue straight ahead (now Aldenham Road) to next roundabout. Take 2nd exit still following Aldenham Road, to next traffic lights. When through lights, move into right-hand lane (marked Watford) and follow one-way around to Bushey Station, then moving into left-hand lane. Turn left under Bushey Arches, into Eastbury Road. At traffic lights turn right into Deacons Hill and continue to next traffic lights, turning left into Cardiff Road for visitors' entrance to stadium/coach park. Straight on for limited off-street parking or car parks in shopping centre; From South: Exit M1 junction 5 take first exit off roundabout, A41 signposted Harrow (then as North); From East: Exit M25 at junction 21A, join the M1 at junction 6. Exit Junction 5 (then as North); From West: Exit M25 junction 19, take 3rd exit at roundabout, A411 (Hempstead Road), signposted Watford. After 2 miles go straight on at roundabout then at next roundabout take 3rd exit, Rickmansworth Road. Take second turning on left into Cassio Road. Through traffic lights, to Merton Road, then Wiggenhall Road. At traffic lights, turn right into Cardiff Road (then as North).

WEST BROMWICH ALBION FC

Founded: 1879
Turned Professional: 1885
Limited Company: 1892
Admitted to League: 1888 (Founder)
Former Name(s): West Bromwich Strollers (1879-1880)
Nickname: 'Throstles' 'Baggies' 'Albion'
Ground: The Hawthorns, Halfords Lane, West Bromwich, West Midlands   B71 4LF

Record Attendance: 64,815 (6/3/37)
Colours: Shirts - Navy Blue & White Stripes
       Shorts - White
Telephone No.: (0121) 525-8888
Ticket Office: (0121) 553-5472
Pitch Size: 115 × 75yds
Ground Capacity: 25,100 (All Seats)

GENERAL INFORMATION
Supporters Club Administrator:
Alan Cleverley
Address: 1 St. Christophers, Hamstead Hill, Handsworth Wood, Birmingham B20 1BP
Telephone Number: (0121) 551-6439
Car Parking: Halfords Lane Car Parks, W.B.B.S. Stand Car Park
Coach Parking: W.B.B.S. Stand Car Park
Nearest Railway Station: Rolfe Street, Smethwick (1.5 miles), Hawthorns (200yds)
Nearest Bus Station: Town Centre
Bus Services to Ground: 74/78/79/450
Club Shop:
Opening Times: Weekdays 9.00-5.00
Saturday Matchdays 9.00-2.45
Telephone No.: (0121) 525-2145
Postal Sales: Yes
Nearest Police Station: Holyhead Road, Handsworth (0.5 mile)
Police Force: West Midlands
Police Telephone No.: (0121) 554-3414

GROUND INFORMATION
Away Supporters' Entrances: Smethwick End
'A' Turnstiles
Away Supporters' Sections: Smethwick End (Covered Seating)
Family Facilities: Location of Stand:
West Bromwich Building Society Family Stand (Home supporters only)
Capacity of Stand: 6,000

ADMISSION INFO (1995/96 PRICES)
Adult Seating: £13.00 - £15.00
Child Seating: £7.00 - £10.00
Programme Price: £1.50
FAX Number: (0121) 553-6634

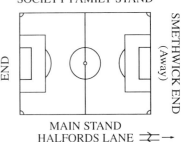

WEST BROMWICH BUILDING SOCIETY FAMILY STAND

BIRMINGHAM ROAD END

SMETHWICK END (Away)

MAIN STAND
HALFORDS LANE

Travelling Supporters Information:
Routes: From All Parts: Exit M5 junction 1 and take Birmingham Road (A41) for Ground.

WEST HAM UNITED FC

Founded: 1895
Turned Professional: 1900
Limited Company: 1900
Admitted to League: 1919
Former Name(s): Thames Iron Works F.C.
Nickname: 'Hammers'
Ground: Boleyn Ground, Green Street,
Upton Park, London   E13 9AZ

Record Attendance: 42,322 (17/10/70)
Colours: Shirts - Claret & Blue
　　　　　　Shorts - White
Telephone No.: (0181) 548-2748
Ticket Office: (0181) 548-2700
Pitch Size: 112 × 72yds
Ground Capacity: 26,014 (All Seats)

GENERAL INFORMATION
Supporters Club Administrator:
Mr. C. Rogers
Address: West Ham Supporters' Club,
Castle Street, East Ham, London   E6 1PP
Telephone Number: (0181) 472-1680
Car Parking: Street Parking
Coach Parking: By Police Direction
Nearest Railway Station: Barking
Nearest Tube Station: Upton Park (5 mins.)
Club Shop: The Hammers Shop
Opening Times: Weekdays & Matchdays
9.30am - 5.00pm
Telephone No.: (0181) 548-2748
Postal Sales: Yes
Nearest Police Station: East Ham High Street
South (0.5 mile)
Police Force: Metropolitan
Police Telephone No.: (0181) 593-8232

GROUND INFORMATION
Away Supporters' Entrances: Turnstiles 1a - 6
Away Supporters' Sections: Centenary Stand
Family Facilities:　**Location of Stand**:
Centenary Upper
Capacity of Stand: 1,900

ADMISSION INFO (1994/95 PRICES)
Adult Seating: £11.00 - £20.00
Child Seating: Concessions in Family Area
Programme Price: £1.50
FAX Number: (0181) 471-2997
Note: For the 1995/96 Season, matches are expected
to be categorised and priced accordingly

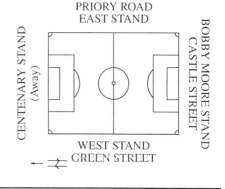

Travelling Supporters Information:
Routes: From North & West: Take North Circular (A406) to A124 (East Ham) then along Barking Road for approximately 1.5 miles until approaching traffic lights at crossroad. Turn right into Green Street, ground is on right-hand side; From South: Take Blackwall Tunnel and A13 to Canning Town. Follow signs for East Ham (A124). After 1.75 miles turn left into Green Street; From East: Take A13 and turn right onto A117 at crossroads. After approximately 1 mile turn left at crossroads onto A124. Turn right (0.75 mile) into Green Street.

WIGAN ATHLETIC AFC

Founded: 1932
Turned Professional: 1932
Limited Company: 1986
Admitted to League: 1978
Former Name(s): None
Nickname: 'Latics'
Ground: Springfield Park, Wigan, Lancs.
WN6 7BA

Record Attendance: 27,500 (12/12/51)
Colours: Shirts - Blue & White Stripes
Shorts - Blue
Telephone No.: (01942) 244433
Ticket Office: (01942) 244433
Pitch Size: 117 × 73yds
Ground Capacity: 6,649
Seating Capacity: 1,100

GENERAL INFORMATION
Supporters Club Administrator: Joe Mills
Address: c/o Club
Telephone Number: (01942) 243512
Car Parking: Street Parking
Coach Parking: Shevington End
Nearest Railway Station: Wallgate & North West (1 mile)
Nearest Bus Station: Wigan
Club Shop:
Opening Times: Weekdays & Matchdays 9.00-5.00
Telephone No.: (01942) 244433
Postal Sales: Yes
Nearest Police Station: Harrogate Street, Wigan (1 mile)
Police Force: Greater Manchester
Police Telephone No.: (01942) 244981

GROUND INFORMATION
Away Supporters' Entrances: Shevington End Turnstiles
Away Supporters' Sections: Shevington End (Partially covered)
Family Facilities: Location of Stand:
In front of Phoenix Stand (Heinz Family Enclosure)
Capacity of Stand: 128

ADMISSION INFO (1995/96 PRICES)
Adult Standing: £6.50
Adult Seating: £8.00
Child Standing: £4.00
Child Seating: £6.00
Programme Price: £1.50
FAX Number: (01942) 2494654

HEINZ
FAMILY
ENCLOSURE
(Disabled)   PHOENIX STAND

SHEVINGTON ROAD
TOWN END

SHEVINGTON ROAD
(Away)

POPULAR SIDE
ST. ANDREWS DRIVE

Travelling Supporters Information:
Routes: From North: Exit M6 junction 27 following signs for Wigan (A5209), turn right (0.25 mile) (B5206). Turn left 1 mile and in 4.5 miles take left into Springfield Road; From South: Exit M6 junction 25 following signs for Wigan (A49). Turn left into Robin Park Road and into Scot Lane. Turn right at 3rd traffic lights into Woodhouse Lane and left at traffic lights into Springfield Road; From East: Take A557 into Town Centre then left into Robin Park Road (then as South).

WIMBLEDON FC

Founded: 1889
Turned Professional: 1964
Limited Company: 1964
Admitted to League: 1977
Former Name(s): Wimbledon Old Centrals
FC (1889-1905)
Nickname: 'Dons'
Ground: Selhurst Park, London   SE25 6PY

Record Attendance: 30,115 (1992-93)
Colours: Shirts - Blue
            Shorts - Blue
Telephone No.: (0181) 771-2233
Ticket Office: (0181) 771-8841
Pitch Size: 110 × 74yds
Ground Capacity: 26,500 (All Seats)

GENERAL INFORMATION
Supporters Club Administrator:
Sue Moody
Address: c/o Club
Telephone Number: (081) 771-2233
Car Parking: Street Parking
Coach Parking: Thornton Heath
Nearest Railway Station: Selhurst/Norwood
Junction (5 minutes walk)
Club Shop:
Opening Times: Weekdays & Matchdays
9.30-5.30
Telephone No.: (081) 653-5584
Postal Sales: Yes
Nearest Police Station: South Norwood
(15 minutes walk)
Police Force: Metropolitan
Police Telephone No.: (081) 653-8568

GROUND INFORMATION
Away Supporters' Entrances: Park Road
Away Supporters' Sections: Corner - Park Road
(Covered Seating)
Family Facilities: Location of Stand:
Members Stand (Clifton Road End)
Capacity of Stand: -

ADMISSION INFO (1995/96 PRICES)
Adult Seating: £10.00 - £20.00
Child Seating: £4.00 - £8.00
Programme Price: £1.50
FAX Number: (0181) 768-0640

Travelling Supporters Information:
Routes: From North: Take M1/A1 to North Circular (A406) to Chiswick. Take South Circular (A205) to
Wandsworth, take A3 to A214 and follow signs to Streatham to A23. Turn left onto B273 (1 mile), follow to
end and turn left into High Street and into Whitehorse Lane; From East: Take A232 (Croydon Road) to
Shirley and join A215 (Norwood Road), after 2.25 miles take left into Whitehorse Lane; From South: Take
A23 and follow signs Crystal Palace B266 through Thornton Heath into Whitehorse Lane; From West: Take
M4 to Chiswick (then as North).

WOLVERHAMPTON WANDERERS FC

Founded: 1877
Turned Professional: 1888
Limited Company: 1892
Admitted to League: 1888 (Founder)
Former Name(s): St. Luke's FC & The Wanderers FC (combined 1880)
Nickname: 'Wolves'
Ground: Molineux Ground, Waterloo Road, Wolverhampton WV1 4QR

Record Attendance: 61,315 (11/2/39)
Colours: Shirts - Gold
Shorts - Black
Telephone No.: (01902) 655000
Ticket Information: (01902) 653653
Pitch Size: 116 × 74yds
Ground Capacity: 28,500 (All Seats)

GENERAL INFORMATION
Members' Club Administrator:
Sue Glover
Address: c/o Commercial Department, Molineux Ground, Waterloo Road, Wolverhampton WV1 4QR
Telephone Number: (01902) 656100
Car Parking: Around West Park & Rear of Stan Cullis Stand
Coach Parking: By Police Direction
Nearest Railway Station: Wolverhamp.(1ml)
Nearest Bus Station: Wolverhamp. (0.25ml)
Bus Services to Ground: 3/503/503A/504/505/506/507/531A/534/535/536/525/525A/682
Club Shop:
Opening Times: Weekdays & Matchdays 9.00-5.00
Telephone No.: (01902) 658777
Postal Sales: Yes
Nearest Police Station: Dunstall Road (500 yds)
Police Force: West Midlands
Police Telephone No.: (01902) 649000

GROUND INFORMATION
Away Supporters' Entrances: Jack Harris Stand Turnstiles Block 5
Away Supporters' Sections: Jack Harris Lower Tier Block 5 or John Ireland Lower Tier, Block 3
Family Facilities: Location of Stand:
Billy Wright Stand - Lower Tier
Capacity of Stand: 2,500

ADMISSION INFO (1995/96 PRICES)
Adult Seating: £9.00 - £14.00
Child Seating: £6.50 - £9.00
Programme Price: £1.50
FAX Number: (01902) 687003
Note: Members receive ticket discounts & other concessions in the Family Area.

MOLINEUX STREET
JOHN IRELAND STAND

STAN CULLIS STAND
NORTH BANK

JACK HARRIS STAND

BILLY WRIGHT STAND
WATERLOO ROAD

Travelling Supporters Information:
Routes: From North: Exit M6 junction 12 following signs for Wolverhampton A5, then A449 and at round-about take 2nd exit into Waterloo Road then turn left into Molineux Street; From South: Exit M5 junction 2 following signs for Wolverhampton A4123, turn right, then left into Ring Road, turn left (1 mile) into Waterloo Road, then turn right into Molineux Street; from East: Exit M6 junction 10 following signs Wolverhampton A454, turn right at crossroads into Stratford Street then turn left (0.25 mile) into Ring Road, right at crossroads into Waterloo Road then right into Molineux Street; From West: Take A454 and at roundabout turn left into Ring Road (then as East).

WREXHAM FC

GENERAL INFORMATION

Supporters Club Administrator:
Miss Ena Williams
Address: c/o Club
Telephone Number: (01978) 262129
Car Parking: Town Car Parks Nearby + Newi
College (Mold End)
Coach Parking: -
Nearest Railway Station: Wrexham
General (Adjacent)
Nearest Bus Station: Wrexham (King Street)
Club Shop: Promotions Office
Opening Times: Office Hours
Telephone No.: (01978) 352536
Postal Sales: Yes
Nearest Police Station: Bodhyfryd (HQ)
(1 mile)
Police Force: Wrexham Division
Police Telephone No.: (01978) 290222

GROUND INFORMATION

Away Supporters' Entrances: Mold End Turnstiles
Away Supporters' Sections: Marstons Stand, Mold
End (Covered)
Family Facilities: Location of Stand:
Yale Stand Town End
Capacity of Stand: 280

ADMISSION INFO (1995/96 PRICES)

Adult Standing: £7.00
Adult Seating: £9.00 or £10.00
Child Standing: £5.00
Child Seating: £7.00
Programme Price: £1.20
FAX Number: (01978) 357821

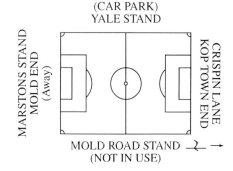

Travelling Supporters Information:
Routes: From North & West: Take A483 and Wrexham Bypass to junction with A541. Branch left and at roundabout follow Wrexham signs into Mold Road; From South & East: Take A525 or A534 into Wrexham then follow A541 signs into Mold Road.

WYCOMBE WANDERERS

Founded: 1884
Former Name(s): None
Nickname: 'The Blues' & 'The Chairboys'
Ground: Adams Park, Hillbottom Road,
Sands, High Wycombe, Bucks
Record Attendance: 9,007 (7/1/95)
vs West Ham United

Colours: Shirts - Dark/Light Blue Quarters
Shorts - Navy Blue
Telephone No.: (01494) 472100
Ticket Office: (01494) 472100
Pitch Size: 115 × 75yds
Ground Capacity: 9,649
Seating Capacity: 1,267

GENERAL INFORMATION

Supporters Club Administrator: None
Address: -
Telephone Number: -
Car Parking: Car Park at Ground (320 cars)
Coach Parking: Car Park at Ground
Nearest Railway Station: High Wycombe
Nearest Bus Station: High Wycombe
Club Shop: At Ground and also in Town
Opening Times: Weekdays & Matchdays
Telephone No.: (01494) 472100 (Ground);
(01494) 450957 (Town Shop)
Postal Sales: Yes
Nearest Police Station: Queen Victoria Road,
High Wycombe (2.5 miles)
Police Force: Thames Valley
Police Telephone No.: (01494) 465888

GROUND INFORMATION

Away Supporters' Entrances: Hillbottom Road End
Away Supporters' Sections: Hillbottom Terrace
Family Facilities: Location of Stand:
Family Section of Main Stand
Capacity of Family Stand: 180

ADMISSION INFO (1995/96 PRICES)

Adult Standing: £7.00
Adult Seating: £10.00 - £12.00
Child Standing: £4.50
Child Seating: £5.00 (Family Stand)
Programme Price: £1.20
FAX Number: (01494) 527633

MAIN STAND
PITCHSIDE ENCLOSURE

BUCKS FREE
PRESS STAND

(AMERSHAM & WYCOMBE COLLEGE END)
HILLBOTTOM ROAD END
(Away)

DAVENPORT VERNON STAND

Travelling Supporters Information:
Routes: Exit M40 junction 4 and take A4010 road following Aylesbury signs. Go straight on at 3 mini-roundabouts and bear sharp left at 4th roundabout into Lane End Road. Fork right into Hillbottom Road at next roundabout. Ground at end. Hillbottom Road on Sands Industrial Estate; From Town Centre: Take A40 West, after 1.5 miles turn left into Chapel Lane (after traffic lights). Turn right then right again at mini-roundabout into Lane End Road - then as above.

YORK CITY FC

<table>
<tr><td>

Founded: 1922
Turned Professional: 1922
Limited Company: 1922
Admitted to League: 1929
Former Name(s): None
Nickname: 'Minstermen'
Ground: Bootham Crescent, York   YO3 7AQ

</td><td>

Record Attendance: 28,123 (5/3/38)
Colours: Shirts - Red
    Shorts - Blue
Telephone No.: (01904) 624447
Ticket Office: (01904) 624447
Pitch Size: 115 × 74yds
Ground Capacity: 10,595
Seating Capacity: 3,248

</td></tr>
</table>

GENERAL INFORMATION
Supporters Club Administrator:
Raymond Wynn
Address: 155 Manor Drive North, York
Telephone Number: (01904) 797578
Car Parking: Street Parking
Coach Parking: By Police Direction
Nearest Railway Station: York (1 mile)
Nearest Bus Station: York
Club Shop:
Opening Times: Monday to Wednesday
9.00-5.00; Thursday 9.00-1.00; Friday 9.00-
3.00; Saturday Matches 1.00-3.00 + 4.40-5.30
Telephone No.: (01904) 645941
Postal Sales: Yes
Nearest Police Station: Fulford
Police Force: North Yorkshire
Police Telephone No.: (01904) 631321

GROUND INFORMATION
Away Supporters' Entrances: Grosvenor Road
Turnstiles
Away Supporters' Sections: Grosvenor Road End,
Bootham Crescent
Family Facilities: Location of Stand:
In front of Main Stand
Capacity of Stand: 164

ADMISSION INFO (1995/96 PRICES)
Adult Standing: £7.00
Adult Seating: £7.00 or £10.00
Child Standing: £4.00 (Members Only)
Child Seating: £4.00 - £6.00 (Members Only)
Programme Price: £1.20
FAX Number: (01904) 631457

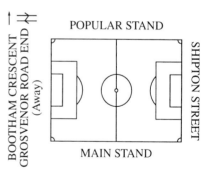

Travelling Supporters Information:
Routes: From North: Take A1 then A59 following York signs. Cross Railway Bridge and turn left (2 miles) into Water End. Turn right at end following City Centre signs for nearly 0.5 mile then turn left into Bootham Crescent; From South: Take A64 and turn left after Buckles Inn on to Outer Ring Road. Turn right onto A19 following City Centre signs for 1.5 miles then turn left into Bootham Crescent; From East: Take Outer Ring Road turning left onto A19 then as South; From West: Take Outer Ring Road turning right on to A19, then as South.

THE F.A. CARLING PREMIERSHIP

and

THE ENDSLEIGH INSURANCE FOOTBALL LEAGUE

STATISTICS

1994-95

F.A. Premiership Season 1994/95

Home \ Away	ARSENAL	ASTON VILLA	BLACKBURN R.	CHELSEA	COVENTRY C.	CRYSTAL PAL.	EVERTON	IPSWICH TOWN	LEEDS UNITED	LEICESTER CITY	LIVERPOOL	MANCHESTER C.	MANCHESTER U.	NEWCASTLE U.	NORWICH CITY	NOTTM. FOREST	Q.P.R.	SHEFFIELD WED.	SOUTHAMPTON	SPURS	WEST HAM UTD.	WIMBLEDON
ARSENAL		0-0	0-0	3-1	2-1	1-2	1-1	4-1	1-3	1-1	0-1	3-0	0-0	2-3	5-1	1-0	1-3	0-0	1-1	1-1	0-1	0-0
ASTON VILLA	0-4		0-1	3-0	0-0	1-1	0-0	2-0	0-0	4-4	2-0	1-1	1-2	0-2	1-1	0-2	2-1	1-1	1-1	1-0	0-2	7-1
BLACK. RVRS.	3-1	3-1		2-1	4-0	2-1	3-0	4-1	1-1	3-0	3-2	2-3	2-4	1-0	0-0	3-0	4-0	3-1	3-2	2-0	4-2	2-1
CHELSEA	2-1	1-0	1-2		2-2	0-0	0-1	2-0	0-3	4-0	0-0	3-0	2-3	1-1	2-0	0-2	1-0	1-1	0-2	1-1	1-2	1-1
COVENTRY CITY	0-1	0-1	1-1	2-2		1-4	0-0	2-0	2-1	4-2	1-1	1-0	2-3	0-0	1-0	0-0	0-1	2-0	1-3	0-4	2-0	1-1
CRYST. PALACE	0-3	0-0	0-1	0-1	0-2		1-0	3-0	1-2	2-0	1-6	2-1	1-1	0-1	0-1	1-2	0-0	2-1	0-0	1-1	1-0	0-0
EVERTON	1-1	2-2	1-2	3-3	0-2	3-1		4-1	3-0	1-1	2-0	1-1	1-0	2-0	2-1	1-2	2-2	1-4	0-0	0-0	1-0	0-0
IPSWICH TOWN	0-2	0-1	1-3	2-2	2-0	0-2	0-1		2-0	4-1	1-3	1-2	3-2	0-2	1-2	0-1	0-1	1-2	2-1	1-3	1-1	2-2
LEEDS UNITED	1-0	1-0	1-2	3-0	3-1	1-4	4-0	2-0		2-1	0-2	2-1	0-0	2-1	1-1	4-0	0-1	0-0	1-1	2-2	3-1	2-1
LEICESTER CITY	2-1	1-1	0-0	1-1	2-2	0-1	2-2	2-0	1-3		1-2	0-1	0-4	1-3	1-0	2-4	1-1	0-1	4-3	3-1	1-2	3-4
LIVERPOOL	3-0	3-2	2-1	3-1	2-3	0-0	0-0	0-1	0-1	2-0		2-0	2-0	2-0	4-0	1-0	1-1	4-1	3-1	1-1	0-0	3-0
MAN. CITY	1-2	2-2	1-3	1-2	0-0	1-1	4-0	2-0	0-0	0-1	2-1		0-3	0-0	2-0	3-3	2-3	3-2	3-3	5-2	3-0	2-0
MAN. UNITED	3-0	1-0	1-0	0-0	2-0	3-0	2-0	9-0	0-0	1-1	2-0	5-0		2-0	1-0	1-2	2-0	2-1	2-1	0-0	1-0	3-0
NEWCASTLE U.	1-0	3-1	1-1	4-2	4-0	3-2	2-0	1-1	1-2	3-1	1-1	0-0	1-1		3-0	2-1	2-1	2-1	5-1	3-3	2-0	2-1
NORWICH CITY	0-0	1-1	2-1	3-0	2-2	0-0	0-0	3-0	2-1	2-1	1-2	1-1	0-2	2-1		0-1	4-2	0-0	2-2	0-2	1-0	1-2
NOTTM. FOREST	2-2	1-2	0-2	3-1	2-1	4-1	2-1	3-0	1-0	1-2	2-1	1-0	1-0	1-0	2-3		3-2	4-1	3-0	2-2	1-1	3-1
Q.P.R.	3-1	2-0	0-1	1-0	2-2	0-1	2-3	1-2	3-2	2-0	2-1	1-2	2-3	3-0	2-0	1-1		3-2	2-2	2-1	2-1	0-1
SHEFF. WED.	3-1	1-2	0-1	1-1	5-1	1-0	0-0	4-1	1-1	1-0	1-2	1-1	1-0	0-0	0-0	1-7	0-2		1-1	3-4	1-0	0-1
SOUTHAMPTON	1-0	2-1	1-1	0-1	0-0	3-1	2-0	3-1	1-3	2-2	0-2	2-2	2-2	3-1	1-1	1-1	2-1	0-0		4-3	1-1	2-3
TOTT. HOTSPUR	1-0	3-4	3-1	0-0	1-3	0-0	2-1	3-0	1-1	1-0	0-0	2-1	0-1	4-2	1-0	1-4	1-1	3-1	1-2		3-1	1-2
WEST HAM UTD	0-2	1-0	2-0	1-2	0-1	1-0	2-2	1-1	0-0	1-0	3-0	3-0	1-1	1-3	2-2	3-1	0-0	0-2	2-0	1-2		3-0
WIMBLEDON	1-3	4-3	0-3	1-1	2-0	2-0	1-1	0-0	2-1	0-0	2-0	0-1	3-2	1-1	2-2	1-3	0-1	0-2	1-2	1-0	2-1	

Team	P	W	D	L	F	A	Pts
Blackburn Rvrs.	42	27	8	7	80	39	89
Manchester Utd.	42	26	10	6	77	28	88
Nott'ham Forest	42	22	11	9	72	43	77
Liverpool	42	21	11	10	65	37	74
Leeds United	42	20	13	9	59	38	63
Newcastle United	42	20	12	10	67	47	72
Tott'ham Hotspur	42	16	14	12	66	58	62
Q.P.R.	42	17	9	16	61	59	60
Wimbledon	42	15	11	16	48	65	56
Southampton	42	12	18	12	61	63	54
Chelsea	42	13	15	14	50	55	54
Arsenal	42	13	12	17	52	49	51
Sheff. Wed.	42	13	12	17	49	57	51
West Ham Utd.	42	13	11	18	44	48	50
Everton	42	11	17	14	44	51	50
Coventry City	42	12	14	16	44	62	50
Manchester City	42	12	13	17	53	64	49
Aston Villa	42	11	15	16	51	56	48
Crystal Palace	42	11	12	19	34	49	45
Norwich City	42	10	13	19	37	54	43
Leicester City	42	6	11	25	45	80	29
Ipswich Town	42	7	6	29	36	93	27

Champions : - Blackburn Rovers

Relegated : - Crystal Palace, Norwich City
Leicester City and Ipswich Town

1st Division Season 1994/95	BARNSLEY	BOLTON W.	BRISTOL C.	BURNLEY	CHARLTON A.	DERBY CO.	GRIMSBY T.	LUTON T.	MIDDLESBR.	MILLWALL	NOTTS CO.	OLDHAM ATH.	PORT VALE	PORTSM'TH	READING	SHEFF. UTD.	SOUTHEND	STOKE CITY	SUND'LAND	SWINDON T.	TRANMERE	WATFORD	WEST BROM.	WOLVES
BARNSLEY		3-0	2-1	2-0	2-1	2-1	4-1	3-1	1-1	4-1	1-1	1-1	3-1	1-0	0-2	2-1	0-0	2-0	2-0	2-1	2-2	0-0	2-0	1-3
BOLTON WANDS.	2-1		0-2	1-1	5-1	1-0	3-3	0-0	1-0	1-0	2-0	2-2	1-0	1-1	1-0	1-1	3-0	4-0	1-0	3-0	1-0	3-0	1-0	5-1
BRISTOL CITY	3-2	0-1		1-1	2-1	0-2	1-2	2-2	0-1	1-0	2-1	2-2	0-0	1-1	1-2	2-1	0-0	3-1	0-0	3-2	0-1	0-0	1-0	1-5
BURNLEY	0-1	2-2	1-1		2-0	3-1	0-2	2-1	0-3	1-2	2-1	2-1	4-3	1-2	1-2	4-2	5-1	1-1	1-1	1-2	1-1	1-1	1-1	0-1
CHARLTON ATH.	2-2	1-2	3-2	1-2		3-4	2-1	1-0	0-2	1-1	1-0	2-0	1-1	1-0	1-1	3-1	0-0	1-0	1-0	0-1	3-0	1-1		3-2
DERBY COUNTY	1-0	2-1	3-1	4-0	2-2		2-1	0-0	0-1	3-2	0-0	2-1	2-0	3-0	1-2	2-3	1-2	3-0	0-1	3-1	5-0	1-1	1-1	3-3
GRIMSBY TOWN	1-0	3-3	1-0	2-2	0-1	0-1		5-0	2-1	1-0	2-1	1-3	4-1	2-0	0-0	4-1	0-0	3-1	1-1	3-1	0-0	0-2	0-2	3-3
LUTON TOWN	0-1	0-3	0-1	0-1	0-1	0-0	1-2		5-1	1-1	2-0	2-1	2-1	2-0	0-1	3-6	2-2	2-3	3-0	3-0	2-0	1-1	1-1	3-3
MIDDLESBRO'	1-1	1-0	3-0	2-0	1-0	2-4	1-1	2-1		3-0	2-1	3-0	4-0	0-1	1-1	1-2	2-1	2-2	3-1	0-1	2-0	2-1	1-0	
MILLWALL	0-1	0-1	1-1	2-3	3-1	4-1	2-0	0-0	0-0		0-0	1-1	1-3	2-2	2-0	2-1	3-1	1-1	2-0	1-1	3-1	2-1	2-2	1-1
NOTTS COUNTY	1-3	1-1	1-1	3-0	3-3	0-0	0-2	0-1	1-1	0-1		1-3	2-2	0-1	1-0	2-1	2-2	0-2	3-2	0-1	1-0	1-0	2-0	1-1
OLDHAM ATH.	1-0	3-1	2-0	3-0	5-2	1-0	1-0	0-0	1-0	0-1	1-1		3-2	3-2	1-3	3-3	0-2	0-0	0-0	1-1	0-0	0-2	1-0	4-1
PORT VALE	2-1	1-1	2-1	1-0	0-2	1-0	1-2	0-1	2-1	1-1	1-1	3-1		1-0	0-2	0-2	5-0	1-1	0-0	2-2	2-0	0-1	1-0	2-4
PORTSMOUTH	3-0	1-1	0-0	2-0	1-1	0-1	2-1	3-2	0-0	3-2	2-1	0-2			1-1	1-0	1-1	0-1	1-4	4-3	1-1	2-1	1-2	1-2
READING	0-3	2-1	1-0	0-0	2-1	1-0	1-1	0-0	1-1	0-0	2-0	2-1	3-3	0-0		1-0	2-0	4-0	0-2	3-0	1-3	4-1	0-2	4-2
SHEFF. UNITED	0-0	3-1	3-0	2-0	2-1	2-1	3-1	1-3	1-1	1-1	1-3	2-0	1-1	3-1	1-1		2-0	1-1	0-0	2-2	2-0	3-0	3-0	3-3
SOUTHEND UTD.	3-1	2-1	2-1	2-1	2-1	1-0	0-0	3-0	0-2	0-1	1-0	1-0	1-2	1-2	4-1	1-3		4-2	0-1	2-0	0-0	0-4	2-1	0-1
STOKE CITY	0-0	1-1	2-1	2-0	3-2	0-0	3-0	1-2	1-1	4-3	2-1	0-1	0-1	0-2	0-1	1-1	4-1		0-1	0-0	1-0	1-0	4-1	1-1
SUNDERLAND	2-0	1-1	2-0	0-0	1-1	1-1	2-2	1-1	0-1	1-1	1-2	0-0	1-1	2-2	0-1	1-0	0-1	1-0		1-0	0-1	1-3	2-2	1-1
SWINDON TOWN	0-0	0-1	0-3	1-1	0-1	1-1	3-2	1-2	2-1	1-2	3-0	3-1	2-0	0-2	1-0	1-3	2-2	0-1	1-0		2-2	1-0	0-0	3-2
TRANMERE R.	6-1	1-0	2-0	4-1	1-1	3-1	2-0	4-2	1-1	3-1	3-2	3-1	1-1	4-2	1-0	2-1	0-2	0-1	1-1	3-2		2-1	3-1	1-1
WATFORD	3-2	0-0	1-0	2-0	2-0	2-1	0-0	2-4	1-1	1-0	3-1	1-2	3-2	2-0	2-2	0-0	1-0	0-0	0-1	2-0	2-0		1-0	2-1
WEST BROM A.	2-1	1-0	1-0	1-0	0-1	0-0	1-1	1-0	1-3	3-0	3-2	3-1	0-0	0-2	2-0	1-0	2-0	1-3	1-3	2-5	5-1	0-1		2-0
WOLVES	0-0	3-1	2-0	2-0	2-0	0-2	2-1	2-3	0-2	3-3	1-0	2-1	2-1	1-0	1-0	2-2	5-0	2-0	1-0	1-1	2-0	1-1	2-0	

Team	P	W	D	L	F	A	Pts
Middlesbrough	46	23	13	10	67	40	82
Reading	46	23	10	13	58	44	79
Bolton Wands.	46	21	14	11	67	45	76
Wolves	46	21	13	12	77	61	76
Tranmere Rovers	46	22	10	14	67	58	76
Barnsley	46	20	12	14	63	52	72
Watford	46	19	13	14	52	46	70
Sheffield United	46	17	17	12	74	55	68
Derby County	46	18	12	16	66	51	66
Grimsby Town	46	17	14	15	62	56	65
Stoke City	46	16	15	15	50	53	63
Millwall	46	16	14	16	60	60	62
Southend United	46	18	8	20	54	73	62
Oldham Athletic	46	16	13	17	60	60	61
Charlton Athletic	46	16	11	19	58	66	59
Luton Town	46	15	13	18	61	64	58
Port Vale	46	15	13	18	58	64	58
Portsmouth	46	15	13	18	53	63	58
West Brom. Alb.	46	16	10	20	51	57	58
Sunderland	46	12	18	16	41	45	54
Swindon Town	46	12	12	22	54	73	48
Burnley	46	11	13	22	49	74	46
Bristol City	46	11	12	23	42	63	45
Notts County	46	9	13	24	45	66	40

PROMOTION PLAY-OFFS

Tranmere Rovers	1	Reading	3
Wolverhampton Wanderers	2	Bolton Wanderers	1

Reading	0	Tranmere Rovers	0

Reading win 3-1 on aggregate

Bolton Wanderers	2	Wolverhampton Wanderers	0

Bolton win 3-2 on aggregate after extra-time. (Normal-time 1-0)

Bolton Wanderers	4	Reading	3

After extra-time. (Normal-time 2-2)

Promoted : - Middlesbrough and Bolton Wanderers

Relegated : - Swindon Town, Burnley, Bristol City and Notts County

2nd Division — Season 1994/95

	BIRMINGHAM	BLACKPOOL	BOURNE'TH	BRADFORD	BRENTFORD	BRIGHTON	BRISTOL R.	CAMBRIDGE	CARDIFF C.	CHESTER C.	CREWE ALEX.	HUDD'FIELD	HULL CITY	LEYTON OR.	OXFORD U.	PETERBORO'	PLYMOUTH A.	ROTHERHAM	SHREWSBURY	STOCKPORT	SWANSEA C.	WREXHAM	WYCOMBE	YORK CITY
BIRMINGHAM C.	■	7-1	0-0	0-0	2-0	3-3	2-0	1-1	2-1	1-0	5-0	1-1	2-2	2-0	3-0	4-0	4-2	2-1	2-0	1-0	0-1	5-2	0-1	4-2
BLACKPOOL	1-1	■	3-1	2-0	1-2	2-2	0-2	2-3	2-1	3-1	0-0	1-4	1-2	2-1	2-1	4-0	5-2	2-2	2-1	1-2	2-1	2-1	0-1	0-5
BOURNEMOUTH	2-1	1-2	■	2-3	0-1	0-3	2-0	1-0	3-2	1-1	1-1	0-2	2-3	2-0	0-2	0-3	0-0	1-1	3-0	2-0	3-2	1-3	2-0	1-4
BRADFORD CITY	1-1	0-1	1-2	■	1-0	2-1	2-1	1-1	2-3	1-1	0-2	3-4	1-0	2-0	0-2	4-2	2-0	0-3	1-1	1-3	1-1	2-1		0-0
BRENTFORD	1-2	3-2	1-2	4-3	■	2-1	3-0	6-0	2-0	1-1	2-0	0-1	0-1	3-0	2-0	0-1	7-0	2-0	1-0	1-0	0-0	0-2	0-0	3-0
BRIGHTON & H.A.	0-1	2-2	0-0	1-0	1-1	■	1-2	2-0	0-0	1-0	0-1	0-0	1-0	1-0	1-1	1-2	1-1	1-1	2-1	2-0	1-1	4-0	1-1	1-0
BRISTOL RVRS.	1-1	0-0	2-1	4-0	2-2	3-0	■	2-1	2-2	3-0	2-2	1-1	0-2	1-0	3-2	3-1	2-0	4-0	2-2	4-0	2-2	1-0		3-1
CAMBRIDGE U.	1-0	0-0	2-2	4-1	0-0	0-2	1-1	■	2-0	2-1	1-2	2-0	1-1	2-1	1-1	2-3	1-1	3-1	3-4	1-3	1-2	2-2		1-0
CARDIFF CITY	0-1	0-1	1-1	2-4	2-3	3-0	0-1	3-1	■	2-1	1-2	0-0	0-2	2-1	1-3	1-2	0-1	1-1	1-2	1-1	1-1	0-0	2-0	1-2
CHESTER CITY	0-4	2-0	1-1	1-4	1-4	1-2	0-0	1-3	0-2	■	0-1	1-2	1-2	2-0	1-1	1-0	4-4	1-3	1-0	2-2	1-1	0-2		0-4
CREWE ALEX.	2-1	4-3	2-0	0-1	0-2	4-0	2-1	4-2	0-0	2-1	■	3-3	3-2	3-0	3-2	2-2	3-1		1-2	3-1	1-3	1-2		2-1
HUDDERSFIELD	1-2	1-1	3-1	0-0	1-0	3-0	1-1	3-1	5-1	5-1	1-2	■	1-1	2-1	3-3	1-2	2-0	1-0	0-2	1-0	2-0	2-1	0-1	3-0
HULL CITY	0-0	1-0	3-1	2-0	1-2	2-2	0-2	1-0	4-0	2-0	7-1	1-0	■	2-0	3-1	1-1	2-0	0-2	2-2	0-0	0-2	3-2	0-0	3-0
LEYTON ORIENT	2-1	0-1	3-2	0-0	0-2	0-3	1-2	1-1	2-0	1-4	0-2	1-1		■	1-1	4-1	0-1		0-1		1-1	0-1		1-1
OXFORD UTD.	1-1	3-2	0-3	1-0	1-1	2-0	1-0	1-0	1-0	2-1	3-1	4-0	3-2		■	1-0	1-0	2-0	4-0	1-2	0-0	0-2	0-2	
PETERBORO' U.	1-1	1-0	0-0	0-0	2-2	2-1	0-0	2-2	2-1	1-5	2-2	2-1	0-0	1-4		■	1-2	2-1	1-1	0-1	1-0	1-0	1-3	1-1
PLYMOUTH ARG.	1-3	0-2	0-1	1-5	1-5	0-3	1-1	0-0	1-0	3-2	0-3	2-1	1-1	0-1			■	0-0	1-0	0-0	2-1	4-1	2-2	1-2
ROTHERHAM U.	1-1	0-2	4-0	3-1	0-2	4-3	0-3	1-1	0-0	1-1	2-2	1-1	2-0	1-1			3-1	■	0-4	1-0	3-3	1-1	3-1	2-0
SHREWSBURY T.	0-2	0-0	3-0	1-2	2-1	1-1	1-0	1-1	0-1	1-1	1-2	2-1	2-3	3-0	1-0	1-2	3-2	1-0	■	1-1	3-3	2-2	2-2	1-0
STOCKPORT CO.	0-1	3-2	1-0	1-2	0-1	2-0	2-1	2-1	4-1	2-2	3-1	1-2	4-0	2-1	0-2	1-1	2-4	1-0	2-1	■	0-1	1-1	4-1	2-3
SWANSEA CITY	0-2	1-0	1-0	0-0	0-2	1-1	1-0	1-0	4-1	0-1	0-1	2-0	3-0	1-0	0-0	2-0					■	0-0	1-1	0-0
WREXHAM	1-1	0-1	2-0	0-1	0-1	2-1	1-1	0-1	0-3	2-2	4-1	3-2	3-3	3-1	3-1	1-1	4-1					■	4-1	1-1
WYCOMBE W.	0-3	1-1	1-1	3-1	4-3	0-0	0-0	3-0	3-1	3-1	0-0	2-1	1-2	2-1	1-0	3-1	1-2	2-0	1-0	1-1	1-0	3-0	■	0-0
YORK CITY	2-0	4-0	1-0	0-0	2-1	1-0	0-3	2-0	1-1	2-0	1-2	3-0	3-1	4-1	2-0	1-1	1-0	3-0	2-4	2-4	0-1	0-0		■

Team	P	W	D	L	F	A	Pts
Birmingham City	46	25	14	7	84	37	89
Brentford	46	25	10	11	81	39	85
Crewe Alex.	46	25	8	13	80	68	84
Bristol Rovers	46	22	16	8	70	40	82
Huddersfield T.	46	22	15	9	79	49	81
Wycombe W.	46	21	15	10	60	46	78
Oxford United	46	21	12	13	66	52	75
Hull City	46	21	11	14	70	57	74
York City	46	21	9	16	67	51	72
Swansea City	46	19	14	13	57	45	71
Stockport County	46	19	8	19	63	60	65
Blackpool	46	18	10	18	64	70	64
Wrexham	46	16	15	15	65	64	63
Bradford City	46	16	12	18	57	64	60
Peterborough U.	46	14	18	14	54	69	60
Brighton & H.A.	46	14	17	15	54	53	59
Rotherham U.	46	14	14	18	57	61	56
Shrewsbury T.	46	13	14	19	54	62	53
Bournemouth	46	13	11	22	49	69	50
Cambridge Utd.	46	11	15	20	52	69	48
Plymouth Argyle	46	12	10	24	45	83	46
Cardiff City	46	9	11	26	46	74	38
Chester City	46	6	11	29	37	84	29
Leyton Orient	46	6	8	32	30	75	26

PROMOTION PLAY-OFFS

Bristol Rovers 0   Crewe Alexandra 0
Huddersfield Town 1   Brentford 1

Crewe Alexandra 1   Bristol Rovers 1
Bristol Rovers win on away goals
Brentford 1   Huddersfield Town 1
Huddersfield Town win 4-3 on penalties after 2-2 aggregate draw

Bristol Rovers 1   Huddersfield Town 2

Promoted : - Birmingham City
and Huddersfield Town

Relegated : - Cambridge United, Plymouth Argyle, Cardiff City, Chester City and Leyton Orient

3rd Division Season 1994/95	BARNET	BURY	CARLISLE UTD.	CHESTERFIELD	COLCHESTER U.	DARLINGTON	DONCASTER R.	EXETER CITY	FULHAM	GILLINGHAM	HARTLEPOOL U.	HEREFORD UTD.	LINCOLN CITY	MANSFIELD T.	NORTHAMPTON	PRESTON N.E.	ROCHDALE	SCARBOROUGH	SCUNTHORPE U.	TORQUAY UTD.	WALSALL	WIGAN ATHLETIC
BARNET	■	1-1	0-2	4-1	0-1	2-3	0-0	1-1	0-0	1-0	4-0	2-2	2-1	2-2	2-3	2-1	6-2	3-1	1-2	2-0	1-3	1-1
BURY	3-0	■	2-0	2-1	4-1	2-1	2-0	0-0	0-0	3-2	2-0	1-1	2-0	2-2	5-0	0-0	0-1	1-0	2-0	3-1	0-0	3-3
CARLISLE UTD.	4-0	3-0	■	1-1	0-0	2-1	1-1	1-0	1-1	2-0	0-1	1-0	1-3	2-1	2-1	0-0	4-1	2-0	2-1	1-0	2-1	2-1
CHESTERFIELD	2-0	0-0	1-2	■	2-2	0-0	2-0	2-0	1-1	2-0	2-0	1-0	1-0	0-1	3-0	1-0	2-2	0-1	3-1	1-0	0-0	0-0
COLCHESTER U.	1-1	1-0	0-1	0-3	■	1-0	0-3	3-1	5-2	2-2	1-0	2-2	1-2	1-1	0-1	3-1	0-0	0-2	4-2	1-3	3-2	0-1
DARLINGTON	0-1	0-2	0-2	0-1	2-3	■	0-2	2-0	0-0	2-0	1-2	3-1	0-0	0-0	4-1	0-0	4-0	1-0	1-3	2-1	2-2	1-3
DONCASTER R.	1-1	1-2	0-0	1-3	1-2	0-0	■	1-0	0-0	1-2	3-0	3-0	3-0	2-0	1-0	2-1	1-0	1-1	1-1	3-0	0-2	5-3
EXETER CITY	1-2	0-4	1-1	1-2	1-0	0-2	1-5	■	0-1	3-0	2-1	1-1	1-0	2-3	0-0	0-1	0-0	5-2	2-2	1-2	1-3	2-4
FULHAM	4-0	1-0	1-3	1-1	1-2	3-1	0-2	4-0	■	1-0	1-0	1-1	1-1	4-2	4-4	0-1	5-0	1-2	1-0	2-1	1-1	2-0
GILLINGHAM	2-1	1-1	0-1	1-1	1-3	2-1	4-2	3-0	4-1	■	0-0	0-0	0-0	3-1	2-3	1-1	3-1	2-2	1-0	1-3	0-1	
HARTLEPOOL U.	0-1	3-1	1-5	0-2	3-1	1-0	2-1	2-2	1-2	2-0	■	4-0	0-3	3-2	1-1	3-1	1-0	3-3	1-4	1-1	1-1	1-0
HEREFORD UTD.	3-2	1-0	0-1	0-2	3-0	0-0	0-1	3-0	1-1	2-1	1-0	■	0-3	0-0	2-1	0-2	0-0	2-1	2-1	1-1	0-0	1-2
LINCOLN CITY	1-2	0-3	1-1	0-1	2-0	3-1	1-0	2-0	2-0	1-1	3-0	2-0	■	3-2	2-2	1-1	2-2	2-0	3-3	1-2	1-1	1-0
MANSFIELD T.	3-0	0-2	1-2	4-2	2-0	0-1	0-1	1-1	1-1	4-0	2-0	7-1	6-2	■	1-1	1-2	1-2	3-1	2-2	1-3	4-3	
NORTHAMPTON	1-1	0-5	2-1	2-3	1-1	2-1	0-0	2-1	0-1	2-0	1-1	1-3	3-1	0-1	■	2-1	1-2	0-3	0-1	2-0	2-2	1-0
PRESTON N.E.	1-0	5-0	1-0	0-0	2-1	1-3	2-2	0-1	3-2	1-1	3-0	4-2	4-0	2-1	2-0	■	3-0	1-0	0-1	0-1	1-2	1-0
ROCHDALE	2-2	0-3	1-2	4-1	0-1	3-1	2-2	0-1	1-2	2-1	1-1	1-3	1-0	3-3	0-0	0-1	■	1-1	1-2	2-0	0-2	1-0
SCARBOROUGH	0-1	1-2	1-2	0-1	0-1	3-1	2-2	0-2	3-1	0-0	2-2	3-1	1-1	2-5	0-0	1-1	2-4	■	3-0	1-1	1-2	0-1
SCUNTHORPE U.	1-0	3-2	2-3	0-1	3-4	2-1	0-5	3-0	1-2	3-0	0-0	1-0	2-0	3-4	1-1	2-1	4-1	3-1	■	3-2	0-1	3-1
TORQUAY UTD.	1-2	2-2	1-1	3-3	3-3	1-0	0-1	0-0	2-1	3-1	2-2	0-1	2-1	2-1	2-1	1-0	4-1	2-1	1-1	■	3-2	0-0
WALSALL	4-0	0-1	1-2	1-3	2-0	2-0	1-0	5-1	2-1	4-1	4-3	2-1	1-0	1-1	2-2	0-0	4-1	2-1	1-0		■	2-0
WIGAN ATH.	1-2	0-3	0-2	2-3	1-2	4-1	3-2	3-1	1-1	0-3	2-0	1-1	0-1	0-4	2-1	1-1	4-0	1-1	0-0	1-1	1-0	■

	P	W	D	L	F	A	Pts
Carlisle United	42	27	10	5	67	31	91
Walsall	42	24	11	7	75	40	83
Chesterfield	42	23	12	7	62	37	81
Bury	42	23	11	8	73	36	80
Preston N.E.	42	19	10	13	58	41	67
Mansfield Town	42	18	11	13	84	59	65
Scunthorpe Utd.	42	18	8	16	68	63	62
Fulham	42	16	14	12	60	54	62
Doncaster Rvrs.	42	17	10	15	58	43	61
Colchester Utd.	42	16	10	16	56	64	58
Barnet	42	15	11	16	56	63	56
Lincoln City	42	15	11	16	53	54	56
Torquay United	42	14	13	15	54	57	55
Wigan Athletic	42	14	10	18	53	60	52
Rochdale	42	12	14	16	47	74	50
Hereford United	42	12	13	17	45	62	49
Northampton T.	42	10	14	18	45	67	44
Hartlepool Utd.	42	11	10	21	43	69	43
Gillingham	42	10	11	21	46	64	41
Darlington	42	11	8	23	43	57	41
Scarborough	42	8	10	24	49	70	34
Exeter City	42	8	10	24	36	70	34

PROMOTION PLAY-OFFS

Mansfield Town 1   Chesterfield 1
Preston North End 0   Bury 1

Chesterfield 5   Mansfield Town 2
Chesterfield win 6-3 on aggregate after extra-time. Normal-time 2-2
Bury 1   Preston North End 0
Bury win 2-0 on aggregate

Bury 0   Chesterfield 2

Promoted : - Carlisle United, Walsall and Chesterfield

Relegated : - No relegation

106

A fresh insight into British football...

THE MONTHLY REVIEW OF BRITISH FOOTBALL

A MONTHLY MAGAZINE PROFILING CLUBS, GROUNDS & PLAYERS

THE PRESENT, THE PAST, THE FUTURE!

- Previews and Reviews
- Football Nostalgia
- Up-to-date Ground Development News
- Statistical Snap-shots
- Scottish & Non-League Sections
- And Much More!

WINGER celebrated its 25th issue in June 1995

What they have said about us : -

"A football fan's delight every month is WINGER" - *Programme Monthly*
"WINGER presents a lively coverage of our game" - *Association of Football Statisticians*
"WINGER is still an excellent publication" - *Football Programme Directory*

Subscription rates for 12 issues: **UK £18** *Overseas £25*

All Cheques payable to WINGER at :

Department S
WINGER
200 BRADFORD ROAD
OTLEY
LS21 3LT
ENGLAND

SEE IT FOR YOURSELF! If you wish to receive WINGER on a trial basis we will send you the current issue plus one extra past issue for £2.
Please send your cheque to the above address.

ENGLAND INTERNATIONAL LINE-UPS AND STATISTICS 1994

9 March 1994
v DENMARK *Wembley*

Seaman	Arsenal
Parker	Manchester United
Adams	Arsenal
Pallister	Manchester United
Le Saux	Blackburn Rovers
Anderton	Tottenham
Platt	Sampdoria
Ince	Manchester United (sub Batty)
Gascoigne	Lazio (sub Le Tissier)
Beardsley	Newcastle United
Shearer	Blackburn Rovers

Result 1-0 Platt

17 May 1994
v GREECE *Wembley*

Flowers	Blackburn Rovers
Jones	Liverpool (sub Pearce)
Adams	Arsenal
Bould	Arsenal
Le Saux	Blackburn Rovers
Anderton	Tottenham (sub Le Tissier)
Richardson	Aston Villa
Merson	Arsenal
Beardsley	Newcastle United (sub Wright)
Platt	Sampdoria
Shearer	Blackburn Rovers

Result 5-0 Anderton, Beardsley, Platt 2 (1 pen), Shearer

22 May 1994
v NORWAY *Wembley*

Seaman	Arsenal
Jones	Liverpool
Bould	Arsenal
Adams	Arsenal
Le Saux	Blackburn Rovers
Anderton	Tottenham (sub Le Tissier)
Ince	Manchester Utd. (sub Wright)
Wise	Chelsea
Platt	Sampdoria
Beardsley	Newcastle United
Shearer	Blackburn Rovers

Result 0-0

7 September 1994
v UNITED STATES *Wembley*

Seaman	Arsenal
Jones	Liverpool
Adams	Arsenal
Pallister	Manchester United
Le Saux	Blackburn Rovers
Venison	Newcastle United
Anderton	Tottenham
Barnes	Liverpool
Platt	Sampdoria
Sheringham	Tottenham (sub Ferdinand)
Shearer	Balckburn Rovers (sub Wright)

Result 2-0 Shearer 2

12 October 1994
v ROMANIA *Wembley*

Seaman	Arsenal
Jones	Liverpool (sub Pearce)
Adams	Arsenal
Pallister	Manchester United
Le Saux	Blackburn Rovers
Ince	Manchester United
Lee	Newcastle United (sub Wise)
Barnes	Liverpool
Le Tissier	Southampton
Wright	Arsenal (sub Sheringham)
Shearer	Blackburn Rovers

Result 1-1 Lee

16 November 1994
v NIGERIA *Wembley*

Flowers	Balckburn Rovers
Jones	Liverpool
Ruddock	Liverpool
Howey	Newcastle United
Le Saux	Blackburn Rovers
Wise	Chelsea
Lee	Newc. Utd. (sub McManaman)
Platt	Sampdoria
Barnes	Liverpool
Beardsley	Newcastle Utd. (sub Le Tissier)
Shearer	Blackburn R. (sub Sheringham)

Result 1-0 Platt

ENGLAND INTERNATIONAL LINE-UPS AND STATISTICS 1995

15 February 1995
v EIRE *Dublin*

Seaman	Arsenal
Barton	Wimbledon
Adams	Arsenal
Pallister	Manchester United
Le Saux	Blackburn Rovers
Ince	Manchester United
Anderton	Tottenham
Platt	Sampdoria
Beardsley	Newcastle United
Le Tissier	Southampton
Shearer	Blackburn Rovers

Result 0-1 (Abandoned after 27 mins - crowd trouble

29 March 1995
v URUGUAY *Wembley*

Flowers	Blackburn Rovers
Jones	Liverpool
Adams	Arsenal
Pallister	Manchester United
Le Saux	Blackburn R. (sub McManaman)
Venison	Newcastle United
Platt	Sampdoria
Anderton	Tottenham
Barnes	Liverpool
Sheringham	Tottenham (sub Cole)
Beardsley	Newcastle United (sub Barmby)

Result 0-0

3 June 1995
v JAPAN *Wembley*

Flowers	Blackburn Rovers
Neville	Manchester United
Scales	Liverpool
Unsworth	Everton
Pearce	Nottingham Forest
Batty	Blackburn R. (sub Gascoigne)
Anderton	Tottenham
Platt	Sampdoria
Beardsley	Newcastle U. (sub McManaman)
Collymore	Nottm. For. (sub Sheringham)
Shearer	Blackburn Rovers

Result 2-1 Anderton, Platt (pen)

8 June 1995
v SWEDEN *Elland Road, Leeds*

Flowers	Blackburn Rovers
Barton	Wimbledon
Cooper	Nottingham Forest
Pallister	Manchester Utd. (sub Scales)
Le Saux	Blackburn Rovers
Anderton	Tottenham
Barnes	Liverpool (sub Gascoigne)
Platt	Sampdoria
Beardsley	Newcastle United (sub Barmby)
Sheringham	Tottenham
Shearer	Blackburn Rovers

Result 3-3 Sheringham, Platt, Beardsley

11 June 1995
v BRAZIL *Wembley*

Flowers	Blackburn Rovers
Neville	Manchester United
Scales	Liverpool (sub Barton)
Cooper	Nottingham Forest
Pearce	Nottingham Forest
Anderton	Tottenham
Platt	Sampdoria
Batty	Blackburn R. (sub Gascoigne)
Le Saux	Blackburn Rovers
Sheringham	Tottenham (sub Collymore)
Shearer	Blackburn Rovers

Result 1-3 Le Saux

72 St. Peters Avenue, Cleethorpes, DN35 8HU, England
24hr orderline (01472) 696226
Faxline (01472) 698546

VHS only

ALL PRICES INCLUDE POSTAGE
UK : Letter Post
Overseas : Airmail Post

10% DISCOUNT ON ALL ORDERS **IN EXCESS OF £60.00**

UK - FORMAT VIDEOS (Suitable for UK, Europe & Australasia)

OFFICIAL HIGHLIGHTS OF THE SEASON

All priced :   £13.99 UK ;   £17.99 Overseas *(including postage)*

1994/95

Arsenal	Aston Villa	Birmingham City
Blackburn Rovers	Chelsea	Derby County
Everton	Leeds United	Liverpool
Manchester City	Manchester United	Middlesbrough
Millwall	Newcastle United	Nottingham Forest
Rangers (Glasgow)	Tottenham Hotspur	West Ham United
	Wolverhampton Wanderers	

THE PAIN AND THE GLORY

Glorious moments with a musical soundtrack.

All priced :   £11.99 UK ;   £15.99 Overseas *(including postage)*

Arsenal	Aston Villa	Chelsea
Everton	Leeds United	Liverpool
Manchester City	Manchester United	Newcastle United
Queen's Park Rangers	Sheffield Wednesday	Southampton
Tottenham Hotspur	West Ham United	

Order From : **The Soccer Bookshelf (Dept SBP)**
72 St. Peters Avenue, Cleethorpes, DN35 8HU, England
Pay By : **Cash/Cheque/Postal Order or**
Credit Card : Access/Mastercard/Barclaycard/Visa/Amex

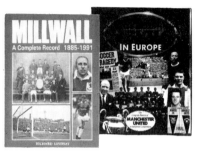

THE PREMIERSHIP AND FOOTBALL LEAGUE GROUNDS

… the book everyone has been waiting for : -

Premiership And 1st Division Football Grounds Before And After Taylor

Featuring FOUR postcard-size full-colour photographs of views from the stands of each Premiership and Endsleigh League 1st Division club - two each from 1991 and 1995.

Printed on high quality art paper

Softback Price £9.99

PUBLISHED OCTOBER 1995

Available from your local bookshop or directly from : -

SOCCER BOOK PUBLISHING LIMITED

(Dept. SBP)

72 St. Peter's Avenue, Cleethorpes, South Humberside, DN35 8HU, ENGLAND

Tel. (01472) 601893   FAX. (01472) 698546

(Postage   £1.00 UK : £1.50 Overseas : £4.00 Airmail)